4th edition

geog.1

teacher's handbook

◆ starters ◆ plenaries ◆ objectives and outcomes
◆ answers ◆ further suggestions for class and homework

<rosemarie gallagher>

OXFORD
UNIVERSITY PRESS

OXFORD
UNIVERSITY PRESS

Great Clarendon Street, Oxford OX2 6DP

Oxford University Press is a department of the University of Oxford.
It furthers the University's objective of excellence in research,
scholarship, and education by publishing worldwide.

Oxford is a registered trade mark of Oxford University Press
in the UK and in certain other countries

Database right Oxford University Press (maker) 2014

First published 2000

Second Edition 2005

Third Edition 2008

Fourth Edition 2014

British Library Cataloguing in Publication Data

Data available

ISBN: 978-0-19-839308-5

10 9 8 7 6 5 4 3 2 1

Printed in Great Britain by Ashford Print and Publishing Services, Gosport

Paper used in the production of this book is a natural, recyclable product made
from wood grown in sustainable forests. The manufacturing process conforms
to the environmental regulations of the country of origin.

Acknowledgements

The publisher would like to thank the following for permission to use
photographs and other copyright material:

Cover image by: Getty (globe); Shutterstock (lemon)

The publisher and author would like to thank the following for their creative
and excellent contributions to the suggestions for starters, plenaries, and
further class and homework:

Richard Parish, Nikki Gowing, Sheila Tucker

Links to third party websites are provided by Oxford in good faith and for
information only. Oxford disclaims any responsibility for the materials
contained in any third party website referenced in this work.

Every effort has been made to contact copyright holders of material
reproduced in this book. Any omissions will be rectified in subsequent
printings if notice is given to the publisher.

Contents

About this course

geog.1 is the first book of *geog.123* – the complete geography course for KS3. The course covers the KS3 Programme of Study, and provides excellent support for assessment.

The course components

The course consists of:

For students

– three students' books – also available as *Kerboodle* online books

– three workbooks

For teachers

– three handbooks

– three *Kerboodles* of online lessons, resources, and assessment, including *Kerboodle* online students' books for teacher access

Find out more about the course components by looking at these panels.

The students' books

- Three books for the course
- Chapters divided into two-page units
- Chapter openers give the big picture – the big ideas behind the chapter – and the goals for the chapter
- Aims of unit given in student-friendly language at the start of each unit
- 'Your turn' questions at the end of each unit

The workbooks

- One for each students' book
- Support for each unit in the students' book
- Fill-in activities
- Ideal for homework and independent study

For more information, see page 17.

The teacher's handbooks

- One for each students' book
- Chapter overviews
- Help at a glance for each unit
- Ideas for starters and plenaries for each unit
- Outcomes for each unit
- Answers for 'Your turn' questions
- Further suggestions for class and homework
- Glossary

geog.123 provides a wide range of materials. The students' books are the core of the course. They combine a rigorous approach to content with a uniquely engaging style.

You can decide how to use the wealth of support materials, but notes in the teacher's handbooks will point you towards appropriate material in the workbooks and *Kerboodle Lessons, Resources, & Assessment*. The result is a truly comprehensive and flexible geography course – which we hope you will enjoy using.

You can access *geog.123* online. There are two purchasable options:

- *Kerboodle Lessons, Resources, & Assessment* (which includes teacher access to the *Kerboodle Book*, an online version of the students' book)
- student access to the *Kerboodle* Book

You can choose to use one or the other, or both – you decide what you and your students need.

Kerboodle Lessons, Resources, & Assessment

- A package to support each students' book
- Lesson presentations and supporting Lesson plans for each unit
- Interactive activities, and animations and video clips
- Editable and photocopiable differentiated Foundation and Extension worksheets for each unit, with answers provided
- Teacher access to the *Kerboodle Book* – the online version of the students' book – for front-of-class use
- Comprehensive support for assessment:
  - interactive auto-marked End-of-lesson assessments, with feedback – one for each unit
  - Extended assessment tasks, with mark schemes – one for each chapter
  - Exam-style questions, with mark schemes – one for each chapter
  - interactive auto-marked Self-assessment forms – one for each chapter
  - markbook and reporting functions
- Many resources are editable
- Upload and create your own content

For more information, see pages 12-16.

Kerboodle Book

- An online version of each of the students' books
- Includes a range of tools that allow students to annotate their book
- Can be accessed on a range of devices with internet connectivity, including iPads and other tablets – so students can have access anywhere, any time

For more information, see page 13.

Using this book

This book aims to save you time and effort! It offers full support for *geog.1* students' book, and will help you prepare detailed course and lesson plans.

What it provides

For each chapter of the students' book, this book provides:

1   a chapter overview
2   help at a glance for each unit, including answers for 'Your turn'
3   further suggestions for class and homework.

It also has a glossary at the back, covering the geographical terms the students will meet.

Please turn to the contents list on page 3 now, to see how this book is structured.
Then find out more about the three main components, below.

1   The chapter overview

This is your introduction to the corresponding students' chapter. Look at its sections.

Shows how the students' chapter relates to the KS3 Programme of Study.

Sets out the objectives and outcomes for the chapter, and the corresponding unit numbers.

Sets out the key ideas within, and behind, the students' chapter. The students' version of this is given in their chapter opening unit.

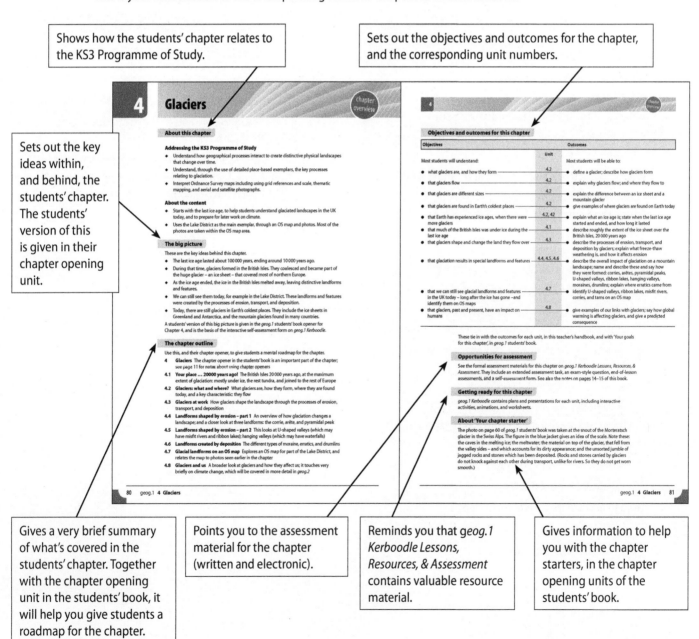

Gives a very brief summary of what's covered in the students' chapter. Together with the chapter opening unit in the students' book, it will help you give students a roadmap for the chapter.

Points you to the assessment material for the chapter (written and electronic).

Reminds you that *geog.1 Kerboodle Lessons, Resources, & Assessment* contains valuable resource material.

Gives information to help you with the chapter starters, in the chapter opening units of the students' book.

2 Help at a glance for each unit

These pages give comprehensive help for each unit of *geog.1* students' book.

> Starts with a brief walk through the unit, to show you how it develops.

> Summarises the key points covered in the unit, plus underlying ideas where appropriate.

> Suggests plenaries for throughout the lesson, not just at the end.

> New vocabulary introduced in the unit. See the glossary at the back of this book.

> A breakdown of the skills practised. It will help you identify where students may need extra support.

> Expected outcomes for the unit. They tie in with the expected outcomes for the chapter.

> Suggestions for starters.

> Points you to related material, including the lesson presentation, interactive activities, worksheets, homework ideas, and assessment opportunities.

> Full answers to the 'Your turn' questions in the students' book, to save you time.

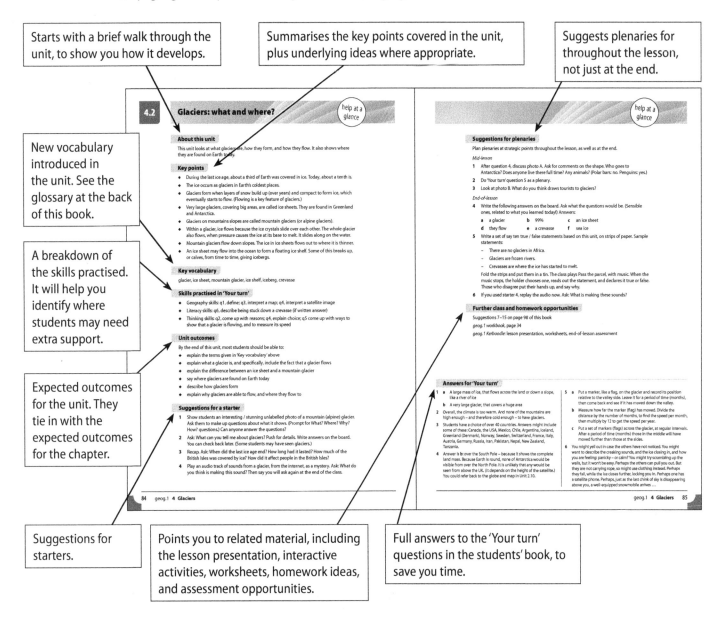

3 Further suggestions for class and homework

These pages give a wealth of further suggestions for class and homework.
They have been graded *, ** or *** according to level of difficulty.
Some are suitable for all levels, and differentiated by outcome.

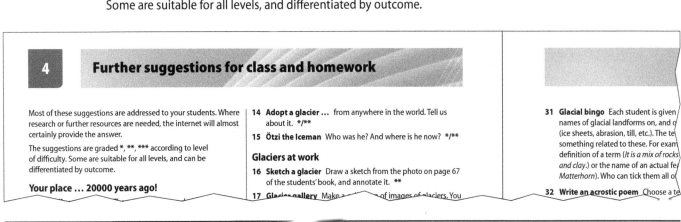

Planning for high-quality lessons

Well-planned and well-structured lessons are a key requirement, for delivering high-quality teaching and learning in any subject, at any level. The *geog.123* course aims to make it easy to plan, structure, and deliver, high-quality lessons for KS3 geography.

Structure of a typical lesson

You will already be familiar with guidelines on structuring lessons. This shows a typical lesson structure.

STARTER

Purpose: To capture students' attention and focus the class. Use it as the lesson hook, or to find out what students know already about a new topic, or for quick revision of earlier work.

INTRODUCTION

Purpose: To prepare students for the activities ahead.

- If this is a new topic, tell students the topic objectives. Write these on the board.
- If it's a continuation of a topic, you can refer back to an objective as appropriate.

ACTIVITIES

This is the main body of the lesson.

Purpose: To achieve one or more of the topic objectives.

- Emphasis on exploration and investigation.
- Provide for practice in different types of skill: geographical, literacy, numeracy, thinking, listening, speaking, team-working, and ICT skills.
- Choose from a variety of activities: reading, answering questions, enquiries, role play, game playing, fieldwork, and ICT.

Plenaries: note that plenaries can be used as staging posts throughout the activities, to gain feedback, check understanding, link to earlier work, and encourage reflection on what is being learnt, and how.

FINAL PLENARY

Purpose: To round off and review what has been done, and to assess what has been achieved against the topic objectives. This is where you help students to:

- check, and crystallise, their understanding
- generalise, for example from an individual case study
- set work in context, and make links to work already done, or to be done in the future
- reflect on how they have learned, as well as what
- check how well they have achieved the topic objectives (self-assessment).

HOMEWORK

Purpose: To confirm, give practice in, and extend, what has been learnt in the lesson.

- The homework can lead on from the final plenary, and be the basis for a starter for the next lesson.

Planning around *geog.1*

Now see how the components of *geog.1* provide material for each part of your lesson.

STARTERS

- The 'Help at a glance' pages in this book have suggestions for lesson starters.
- See further notes about starters, and resources for them, in this book.

OBJECTIVES

- The opening lines of each unit in the students' book give the purpose of the unit, in student-friendly language. The goals for each chapter are given in its opening unit.
- See also the objectives and outcomes given in this book.

ACTIVITIES

Using the students' book

- The text in the students' book provides the core information students need. Some lends itself to reading aloud, but try 'quiet time' too.
- You can let students work through the text uninterrupted, or break it up with 'Your turn' questions. (These generally follow the order of the text.)
- The questions give practice in literacy, numeracy, thinking, and geography skills.
- Some are ideal as whole-class questions with verbal response. Others can be worked through by students working alone, in pairs, or in small groups. The final 'Your turn' questions are usually open questions that challenge students to show what they can do.
- For students who finish early, check out 'Further suggestions for class and homework' at the end of each chapter in this book. Or select a worksheet from the *Kerboodle Lessons, Resources, & Assessment*.

Using *Kerboodle Lessons, Resources, & Assessment*

- The *Kerboodle Lessons, Resources, & Assessment* gives you a ready-to-play lesson presentation (with teacher's notes) for each unit plus interactive activities, animations and video clips.
- The *Kerboodle* also offers differentiated Foundation and Extension worksheets and an End-of-lesson interactive assessment (with feedback) for each unit.
- Much of the material is suitable for whole-class teaching using an interactive whiteboard or projector, and offers scope for vibrant and effective lessons.

PLENARIES

- The 'Help at a glance' pages in this book give suggestions for plenaries, for throughout the lesson as well as at the end.
- See further notes about plenaries, and resources for them, in this book.

HOMEWORK

- 'Further suggestions for class and homework' at the end of each chapter in this book offer lots of ideas.
- Select a worksheet from the *Kerboodle Lessons, Resources, & Assessment*.
- The workbook provides support for every unit in the students' book.
- Use the End-of-lesson interactive assessment for each unit on the *Kerboodle Lessons, Resources, & Assessment*.
- Use other assessment materials on the *Kerboodle Lessons, Resources, & Assessment* – the Extended assessment tasks and/or the Exam-style questions.

More about starters and plenaries

Planning your starters and plenaries

Effective starters and plenaries need to be planned for. With planning, you can ensure that they'll help you to meet your lesson objectives, and that you won't have to rely on sudden inspiration in the classroom. But even where they are planned, you may want and need to modify them as you go along, in response to your students.

Our suggestions for starters and plenaries

The kinds of activities you feel comfortable with, for starters and plenaries, will depend on your teaching style, and the individual class. So the suggestions for starters and plenaries in this book are just that: suggestions! You may want to use some as described, or adapt them. Or they may provide inspiration for new ideas of your own.

The starters

- Most of these are intended for use with the students' books closed, before students have looked at the new unit. But they lead seamlessly into the work in the students' book.

- In some cases you may want to combine two starters to give a more extended one.

- A number of starters require the use of an atlas, and can be an excellent way of giving your students atlas practice that's fun.

- Other starters require both physical and mental activity – for example creating a graffiti wall on the board. This is a good way to get everyone involved.

The plenaries

- There are suggestions for plenaries for throughout the lesson, not just at the end.

- They have been chosen for a variety of purposes: to encourage feedback; assess understanding; promote reflection; build bridges with material already covered (or still to be covered), with other subjects, and with the real world; help crystallise what has been learnt; and see whether it applies to other situations.

- Some of the plenaries are single questions. You will find that you can readily combine some to make more extended plenaries.

- Some need more preparation than others. You might not want to choose these for every class, but it's a good idea to ring the changes, and keep your students surprised.

- Together with 'Your turn', the 'Ideas for plenaries' section is a rich resource to help you deliver fresh, exciting, and effective lessons.

Resources for starters and plenaries

Images

Many of the starters, and some plenaries, require images – mostly photos. There's a wealth of useful resources on the *Kerboodle Lessons, Resources, & Assessment*. You could use some of these to design your own starters or plenaries.

The interactive activities and animations and video clips on the *Kerboodle Lessons, Resources, & Assessment* also make great starters and plenaries.

The internet, of course, is an excellent source for other geographical photos and images. Please check with the appropriate people in your school regarding copyright issues.

Building a resource library

Some resources, such as photos, can be used over and over. You may want to create your own resource library. Laminating printed photos, and other resources (such as True/False cards), will extend their lives and save you time and effort in the future.

Using the chapter openers in the students' book

The chapter openers in the students' book are in effect the starters for new topics – and you can return to them as an end-of-topic plenary.

Below is a typical chapter opener.

Large photo to hook your students' attention (we hope!). The opening photos usually relate to specific material within the chapter, and are referred back to, at different points.

Gives the big underlying ideas for the chapter. These provide the context for new learning. At the end of the chapter they can be reviewed, to help crystallise the learning.

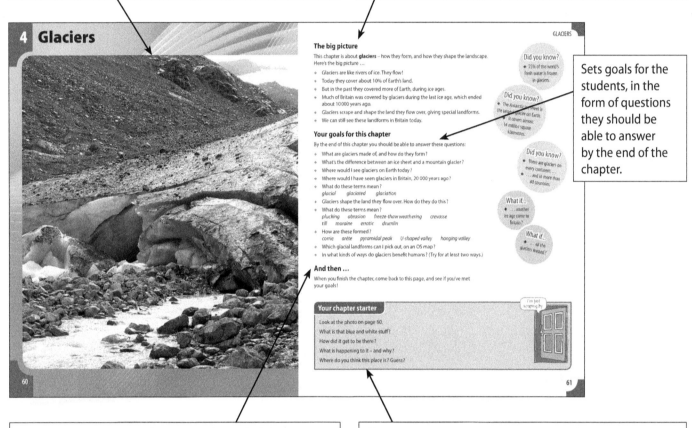

Sets goals for the students, in the form of questions they should be able to answer by the end of the chapter.

Invites students to revisit the goals at the end of the chapter. Note that the *Kerboodle Lessons, Resources, & Assessment* has an interactive students' Self-assessment form for each chapter, which refers to these goals.

Chapter starter questions, to get your students thinking. The 'Chapter overviews' in this book give information about the photos (where available), and some background for the starter questions.

Using the chapter openers

As you can see, the chapter openers can do quite a lot of useful work, so it's worth spending some time on them.

- 'The big picture' can be read aloud, and discussed.

- You can work through 'Your goals for this chapter' in advance, to find out what students know already. Most will probably be able to answer at least a couple of questions.

- Using the teacher-access *Kerboodle Book* in *Kerboodle Lessons, Resources, & Assessment*, you could display the chapter openers on the whiteboard.

- For some of the chapter starters (but not all) there are suggestions for related work, in the 'Further suggestions for class and homework' pages in this book.

- Then the next step is to give students a mental roadmap for the chapter, using the corresponding 'Chapter overviews' in this book.

Kerboodle is an online resource. It offers two purchasable options:

- *Kerboodle Lessons, Resources, & Assessment* (which includes teacher access to the *Kerboodle Book*)
- student access to the *Kerboodle Book* – an online version of the students' book

You can choose to use one or the other or both – you decide what you and your students need. Each option is available as an annual licence for unlimited users.

Kerboodle Lessons, Resources, & Assessment

Lessons

There's a Lesson presentation for each unit in the students' book. There are resources attached to each presentation – including interactives, animations and videos, and worksheets. Each Lesson presentation is supported by a Lesson plan.

For each unit, the Lesson presentation provides engaging coverage of a particular learning objective – a key point or idea, or an important concept. It is provided to help you with part of the lesson – it is not intended to be the whole lesson.

You can add your own material to the Lesson presentations and the Lesson plans.

Front-of-class resources – interactives, animations and videos – are built into each presentation, helping you to create lively lessons.

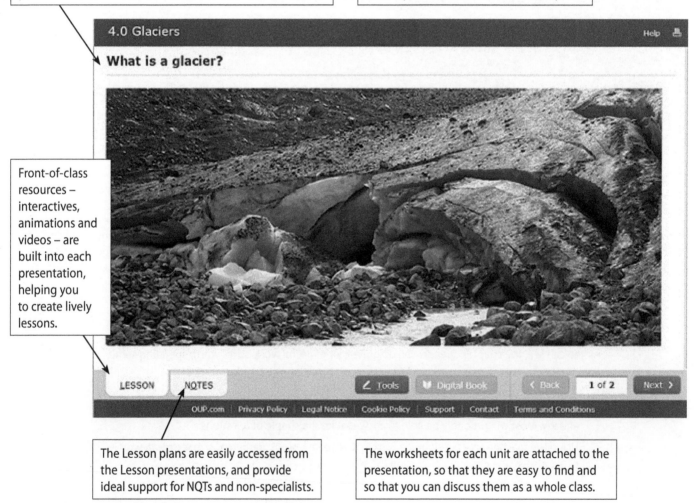

The Lesson plans are easily accessed from the Lesson presentations, and provide ideal support for NQTs and non-specialists.

The worksheets for each unit are attached to the presentation, so that they are easy to find and so that you can discuss them as a whole class.

Resources

Kerboodle includes a wealth of resources – you can use them as part of the Lesson presentations, or on their own as stand-alone resources to suit your particular needs.

*   Resources include items for front-of-class use, such as whole-class interactive activities and animations and videos.

*   Resources include differentiated worksheets that can be printed off and photocopied for use in class or homework – please see page 16 for more information and samples.

*   Teacher access to the *Kerboodle Book* is provided for front-of-class use. This allows you to focus your students' attention on particular maps, diagrams, or photos, or on particular pieces of text, during your lesson. You can use a range of tools as part of this, and you can save any annotations.

*   Upload your own resources – so that you can personalise your course.

Assessment

There's a comprehensive and flexible assessment package – please see pages 14-15 for details.

Kerboodle Book

The *Kerboodle Book* is an online version of the students' book.

Student access includes a range of tools that allow students to annotate their book.

Teacher access is included as part of the *Kerboodle Lessons, Resources, & Assessment* for front-of-class use.

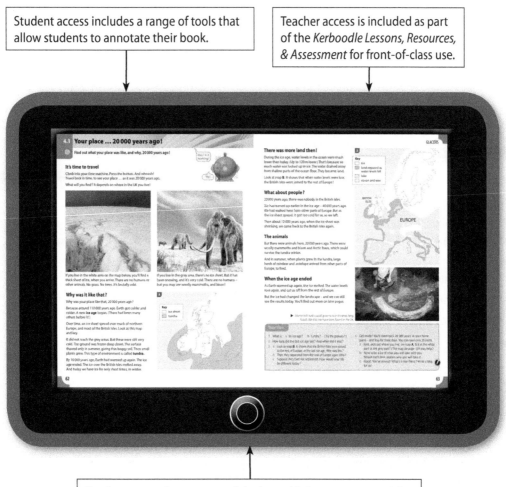

Can be accessed on a range of devices with internet connectivity, including iPads and other tablets – so students can have access anywhere, any time.

About assessment on *Kerboodle*

We hope the assessment package on *Kerboodle Lessons, Resources, & Assessment* will help you – whatever your approach to assessment, and however your school measures progress.

The comprehensive support for assessment includes:

- End-of-lesson assessments with feedback
- Extended assessment tasks with mark schemes
- Exam-style questions with mark schemes
- Self-assessment forms
- markbook and reporting functions

End-of-lesson assessments

There's an End-of-lesson assessment for each unit (double-page spread) in the students' book.

These are interactive, multi-question multi-screen formative assessments – students complete the questions on-screen, and receive feedback after each question. The questions focus on the content of the unit, and help test core knowledge.

Each assessment should take most students about thirty minutes to complete, and can be done either in class or for homework; they could be used promptly after the lesson, or some time later.

These assessments are auto-marked, with feedback, and the student outcome is given as a percentage and automatically entered into the markbook.

Extended assessment tasks

There's an Extended assessment task for every chapter in the students' book. Each consists of:

1. a presentation of the task and mark scheme, on-screen, for front-of-class use (see panel)
2. teacher notes, on paper, including the mark scheme and sample answers at two levels
3. student assessment material, on paper, including a student-friendly version of the mark scheme to help them achieve and progress

These are substantial pieces of work for students, and the tasks vary – they include decision-making exercises, enquiries, and extended writing.

You will need a lesson or part of a lesson to brief the task to your students. Most students will then need approximately two hours to complete the task.

The task is marked by you, using the mark scheme provided. Each mark scheme uses specially-written descriptors built around Bloom's Taxonomy and allows for student outcome to be given in terms of:

- a performance term (beginning/developing, securing, extending)
- a GCSE grade indicator
- or a level developed from the old National Curriculum Levels

You can easily convert the mark to a score so that it can be entered into the markbook.

The digital front-of-class presentations help you brief your students – you can:

- explain the task or question
- identify and explain the command language
- look at the mark scheme
- and view sample answers

– so that you can help students understand what's required, and how they can be successful.

Exam-style questions

These are KS3-appropriate. There's one Exam-style question per chapter. Each consists of:

1 a presentation of the question and mark scheme, on-screen, for front-of-class use (see panel)

2 teacher notes, on paper, including the mark scheme, guidance for adapting the question for lower and higher ability students, and sample answers at two levels

3 student question sheet(s), on paper

You will need part of a lesson to brief your students. Most students will then need approximately twenty minutes to write their answers.

The question is marked by you, using the mark scheme provided. Each mark scheme uses specially-written descriptors built around Bloom's Taxonomy – the mark scheme allows for student outcome to be given in terms of:

• a performance term (beginning/developing, securing, extending)

• a GCSE grade indicator

• or a level developed from the old National Curriculum Levels

You can easily convert the mark to a score so that it can be entered into the markbook.

Self-assessment forms

There's a Self-assessment form for every chapter in the students' book.

These are based on the 'Your goals for this chapter' on the chapter-opening spreads. They are completed on-screen, and should take about ten minutes. They are auto-marked, with the student response feeding automatically into the markbook.

The markbook

The markbook allows you to easily record and track progress.

For the End-of-lesson assessments and Self-assessment forms, student scores and responses are automatically recorded in the markbook. For the Extended assessment tasks and Exam-style questions, you can manually enter scores (the markbook records percentages only to allow quick comparison of performance) – guidance on how to do this is provided.

The markbook reporting functionality allows you to run reports on individual students, classes, and year groups across a single assessment or multiple assessments. You can also run diagnostic reports on the auto-marked assessments to see question-by-question performance across a group.

About the *geog.1* worksheets

geog.1 Kerboodle Lessons, Resources, & Assessment provides differentiated Foundation and Extension worksheets for each unit in the students' book. Answers are also provided.

Worksheets can be printed and photocopied – so they are ideal for cover lessons and homework.

The two worksheets for each unit are attached to the Lesson presentation – so you can see at a glance what's available to support that lesson. They can also be accessed as a separate *Resource* type.

Worksheets can be displayed on the whiteboard, allowing you to discuss questions with students.

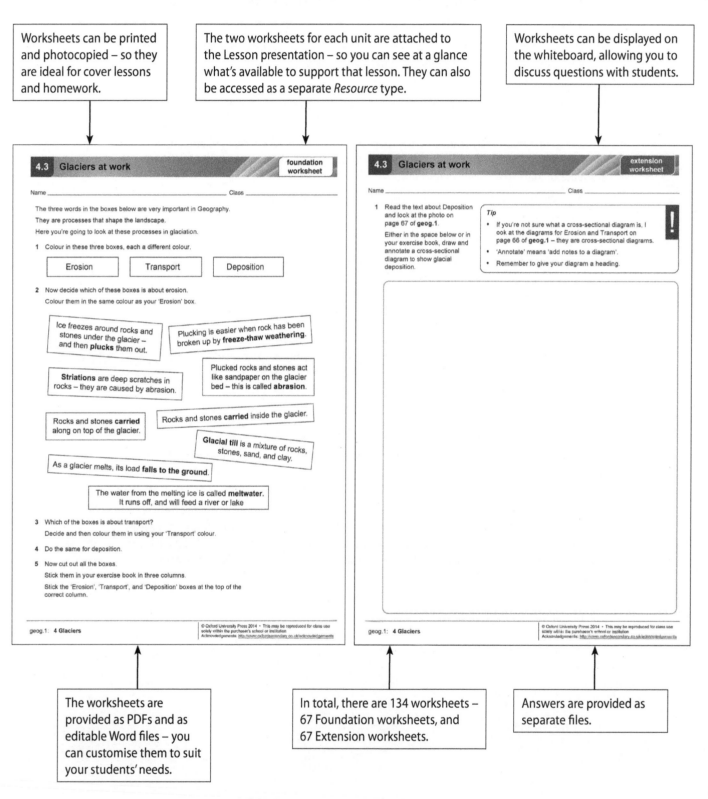

The worksheets are provided as PDFs and as editable Word files – you can customise them to suit your students' needs.

In total, there are 134 worksheets – 67 Foundation worksheets, and 67 Extension worksheets.

Answers are provided as separate files.

About *geog.1 workbook*

The *geog.1 workbook* provides support for every unit (double-page spread) in the *geog.1* students' book.

The activities focus on core knowledge, locational knowledge, and skills. The workbook is ideal for homework.

A page of fill-in activities for every double-page spread in the students' book, to hand when you need it.

Perfect for homework and independent study, and great for cover lessons.

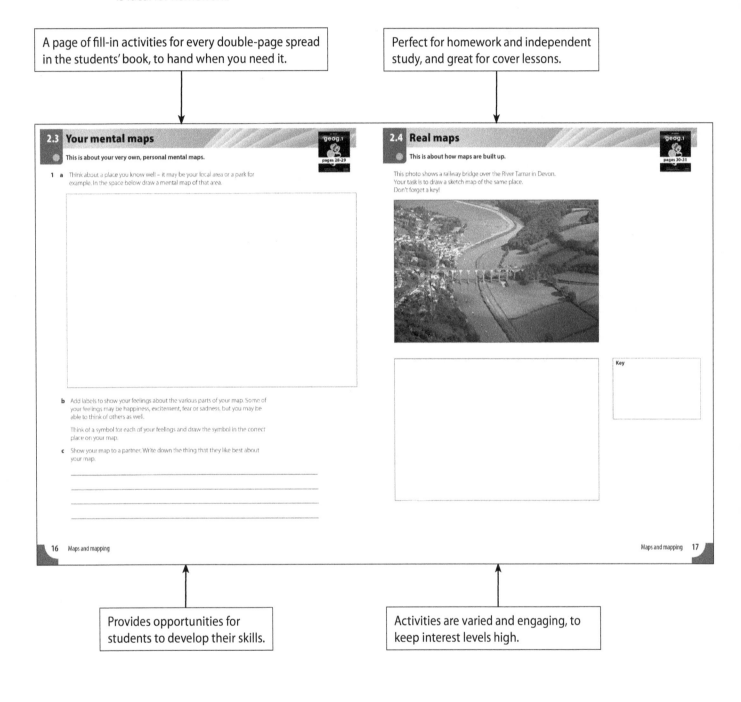

Provides opportunities for students to develop their skills.

Activities are varied and engaging, to keep interest levels high.

1 It's your planet!

About this chapter

Addressing the KS3 Programme of Study

◆ *geog.123* aims to help teachers meet the stated purpose of the Programme of Study:

A high-quality geography education should inspire in students a curiosity and fascination about the world and its people that will remain with them for the rest of their lives.

◆ Chapter 1 provides a broad introduction to this education.

About the content

◆ The chapter starts at the very beginning: the Big Bang! It describes how Earth formed, and when, and how life developed.

◆ This early starting point allows us to introduce and set in context several topics and themes which we will return to later. These include: geographical timescales, ice ages, volcanic activity, human migration, and how physical and human processes are changing Earth.

The big picture

These are the key ideas in this chapter.

◆ Earth's story began with the Big Bang, about 13.8 billion years ago. Earth itself was formed, as part of the solar system, around 4.5 billion years ago.

◆ Life developed over the last 3.5 billion years. Starting from single cells, hundreds of millions of species evolved (most now extinct).

◆ We have learned a great deal about Earth's story from the study of rocks and fossils. That knowledge has been summarised to give the geological timescale.

◆ We humans (*Homo sapiens*) appeared only about 200 000 years ago, in East Africa. We began spreading around Earth only about 60 000 years ago.

◆ Earth is being continually changed by natural processes.

◆ We are changing it too. We have spread over most of Earth, farming it, mining it, building on it, and carving it up into nearly 200 countries. We have had a huge impact.

◆ Many of our activities have been harmful to ourselves and to other species.

A students' version of this big picture is given in the *geog.1* students' book opener for Chapter 1, and is the basis of the interactive self-assessment form on *geog.1 Kerboodle*.

The chapter outline

Use this, and their chapter opener, to give students a mental roadmap for the chapter.

1   It's your planet! The chapter opener in the students' book is an important part of the chapter; see page 11 for notes about using chapter openers

1.1 Earth's story: it begins with a bang From the Big Bang, through the birth of our solar system, to the first living cells

1.2 Earth's story: life develops How cells evolved, and increasingly complex species developed; and eventually we appeared – *Homo sapiens*

1.3 Earth's story: the timescale A simplified version of the geological timescale, which summarises what we have learned of Earth's history through the study of rocks and fossils

1.4 Our time on Earth If 12 hours represent Earth's age, we arrived only 2 seconds ago!

1.5 Our place on Earth About a sense of place, with photos as stimuli

1.6 Earth: a very special planet Earth, its place in the solar system, and its species today

1.7 Changing Earth Introduces two key concepts which we'll revisit very often: Earth is being changed by natural processes, and by human activities

1.8 It's all geography! Introduces three strands of geography – physical, human and environmental – and the idea of the geographer as a nosy detective

Objectives and outcomes for this chapter

Objectives	Unit	Outcomes
Most students will understand:		Most students will be able to:
that Earth is part of our solar system, which has the Sun at its centre	1.1, 1.6	describe how Earth was formed; say where Earth is in the solar system; give Earth's age
that the geological timescale sums up what we have learned about Earth's history	1.3	explain what the geological timescale is; say the information came from studying rocks and fossils; say what the pre-Cambrian era is, and what life existed then; give one fact about each of these periods: the Carboniferous, Permian, Jurassic, and Quaternary
that the theory of evolution is widely accepted	1.2	describe the process of evolution in a simple way; say that the first living things were single cells; say that not everyone accepts the theory of evolution
that we modern humans (*Homo sapiens*) are relatively recent arrivals	1.2, 1.4	say that we first appeared in East Africa around 200 000 years ago – or only 2 seconds ago, relative to Earth's age as shown on a 12-hour clock
that we started spreading around Earth about 60 000 years ago	1.4	describe briefly how we spread; that it was during an ice age; that we first arrived in Britain around 40 000 years ago, left because it got too cold, and returned around 12 000 years ago
that we live in some very different places today	1.5	give examples of different places; begin to describe their own place
that Earth is being changed by both natural processes and human activities	1.7	give three examples of natural processes that change Earth, and three examples of changes brought about by humans
that geography can be divided into different kinds	1.8	name physical, human, and environmental geography as three strands of geography; give examples of at least two topics for each strand
that good geographers are observant and full of curiosity	1.8	come up with at least four questions (Who, What, Why … type of questions) about a photo or situation

These tie in with the outcomes for each unit, in this teacher's handbook, and with 'Your goals for this chapter', in *geog.1* students' book.

Opportunities for assessment

See the formal assessment materials for this chapter on *geog.1 Kerboodle Lessons, Resources, & Assessment*. They include an extended assessment task, an exam-style question, end-of-lesson assessments, and a self-assessment form. See also the notes on pages 14–15 of this book.

Getting ready for this chapter

geog.1 Kerboodle contains plans and presentations for each unit, including interactive activities, animations, and worksheets.

About 'Your chapter starter'

The image on page 4 of *geog.1* students' book shows planet Earth from space. The thin blue halo is our atmosphere. Earth is the third planet out from the Sun, and is held in its orbit around the Sun by gravitational attraction (gravity). It is about 150 million km from the Sun, and takes 365.25 days to travel all the way round it. And as it travels it spins on its axis, taking 24 hours for a complete spin. We don't yet know of life on any other planet in the solar system – or anywhere else in the Universe. But we have our suspicions!

1.1 Earth's story: it begins with a bang

help at a glance

About this unit

Starting with the Big Bang, this unit tells how Earth formed, and how life began.

Key points

- The Big Bang was a violent explosion of energy. It occurred about 13.8 billion years ago. It was the start of the Universe.
- Earth formed about 4.5 billion years ago, from dust and gases swirling around a new-born star, our Sun. The dust and gases were pulled together by the force of gravity.
- We think that the moon is the result of another planet striking the soft Earth. The impact flung material into space, and it then coalesced.
- As Earth cooled, its crust hardened, and water vapour condensed to form the oceans.
- The first living cells appeared about 3.5 billion years ago in the ocean, perhaps as a result of substances carried on meteorites, falling from space.
- Those cells evolved over time into different living things, in a process called evolution.
- The theory of evolution is widely accepted – but not by everyone.
- Theories are not the same as facts. They fit the available evidence – but new evidence might prove them wrong.

Key vocabulary

Big Bang, Sun, planet, Earth, moon, atmosphere, ocean, evolve, evolution, fact, theory

Skills practised in 'Your turn'

- Literacy skills: q1, define
- Thinking skills: q2, explain how Earth was formed; q3, put events in the correct order; q4, differentiate between fact and theory; q5, consider the Big Bang theory versus belief in God's creation

Unit outcomes

By the end of this unit most students should be able to:

- explain the terms given in 'Key vocabulary' above
- describe how Earth was formed, and say how old it is
- say that the first life was tiny single cells which could reproduce themselves
- describe, in a simple way, the process of evolution

Ideas for a starter

1 Look at the image of Earth, on page 4 of the students' book (or display it). Ask: How do you think it was taken? Who might have taken it? Where from? What's all the dark blue stuff? Can you name the large area of dark blue, on the left? What's the white wispy stuff? Where are you on the image?

2 Look at the image of Earth, on page 4 of the students' book (or display it). Ask students to write down three facts about planet Earth. Compile a list of facts on the whiteboard.

3 Ask: How did Earth get here?

4 In the news: Find an exciting news story about the solar system. Read the story. What other stories have students read about or seen? You could prompt them with key words or ideas about recent events. Play a short film clip showing Earth from space, such as *Pale Blue Dot*, narrated by Carl Sagan.

Ideas for plenaries

Plan plenaries at strategic points throughout the lesson, as well as at the end.

Mid-lesson

1   Clarify students' understanding of 'a fact' and 'a theory'.

2   Explain: Everything is attracted to everything else by a gravitational force. We usually call it just gravity. You don't notice it for little things. But when one of the things has enormous mass, like Earth, you notice it a lot. Ask: Who can demonstrate that we are attracted to Earth by gravity? Students could jump up, or throw something up. All fall back to Earth again. This could lead to discussion of the attraction between Earth and the Sun, and Earth and the moon.

3   What if Earth had not been bombarded by meteorites?

End-of-lesson

4   Ask students to imagine travelling back in time 4 billion years to find Earth's crust covered with volcanoes. Prompt for adjectives to describe what Earth is like.

5   Write each of the eight statements about Earth's story in 'Your turn' question 3 on to a separate card. Give one card to each of eight students, and ask all eight to stand in a line from right to left, facing the class, in the order they think these eight events happened. Others in the class can tell them to change places if they think the order is wrong. When they are in the right place, each cardholder reads out their event in turn.

6   Write the word 'Evolution' on the whiteboard. Students can vote as to whether they think this is a fact or a theory. Can anyone justify their opinion?

Further class and homework opportunities

Suggestions 1–6 on page 36 of this book

geog.1 workbook, page 5

geog.1 Kerboodle: see lesson presentation, worksheets, end-of-lesson assessment

Answers to 'Your turn'

1   A violent explosion of energy, around 13.8 billion years ago, that led to the formation of the Universe, and matter.

2   It formed when dust and gases whirling around the Sun were drawn together by gravity to form rocks; then the rocks fused to form Earth (and other planets).

3   The order of entries in the flow chart should be: the Big Bang, our Sun formed, Earth formed, our moon formed, Earth's surface cooled, the ocean formed, living cells appeared.

4   a   A theory; it fits the evidence, but nobody was there to see it. (Evidence includes: the way the moon orbits Earth; the fact that isotopes (different types of the same atom) are in exactly the same ratio on the moon as on Earth.)

    b   A fact; rain can be tested in many different ways, to prove it is water. For example, by measuring its boiling and freezing points, or by carrying out chemical tests.

5   This should prompt some discussion. Students might conclude that the Big Bang could be seen as God's way of creating the Universe. You could point out that many scientists who accept the Big Bang theory also believe in God. But many people who believe that God created the Universe reject the Big Bang theory.

Earth's story: life develops

help at a glance

About this unit

This unit tells the story of how life evolved from simple cells, with more and more complex species appearing – and, eventually, there was us.

Key points

◆ For over 2 billion years, the only life on Earth was cells in the ocean.

◆ Over time, simple single cells evolved into more complex cells, and eventually different types of cells joined, to form the first soft-bodied animals.

◆ Over millions of years, more and more species appeared in the ocean.

◆ Then about 475 million years ago, life moved from the ocean onto land, when simple plants evolved from algae.

◆ The first animals moved onto land around 395 million years ago.

◆ Evolution continued on land and in the ocean, but periodic mass extinctions killed off many millions of species. Only those that survived could continue to evolve. The rest disappeared forever.

◆ The first species of human appeared about 2 million years ago in East Africa. Modern humans (*Homo sapiens*) appeared about 200 000 years ago. (So we've been on Earth for only a fraction of the time the dinosaurs were.)

◆ We learn about when plants and animals appeared, and became extinct, through the study of fossils, and the layers of rock they are found in.

Key vocabulary

mass extinction, asteroid, *Homo sapiens,* fossil

Skills practised in 'Your turn'

◆ Numeracy skills: q3, subtraction

◆ Literacy skills: q1, q2, unjumble terms, and write them out with their definitions; q6, describe an imaginary mass extinction

◆ Thinking skills: q7, come up with predictions about future human species

Unit outcomes

By the end of this unit most students should be able to:

◆ explain the terms given in 'Key vocabulary' above

◆ explain what a mass extinction is

◆ state when and where we (*Homo sapiens)* first appeared

◆ describe the process of evolution in a simple way

◆ explain what we can learn from fossils

Ideas for a starter

1 Recap. Draw a timeline on the whiteboard which includes key dates from Unit 1.1: 13.8 billion years ago (The Big Bang); 4.6 billion years ago (the Sun was born in the Milky Way); 4.5 billion years ago (Earth formed); 3.5 billion years ago (the first living cells on Earth); Today (we are here!). Ask students to identify and add the main events (in brackets above) which happened at each of these key dates.

2 Recap. Write the following words on the board in a random order: Universe, galaxy, Earth, moon, meteorite. Ask students to rank them in order of size, starting with the smallest.

3 Bring in a visual stimulus, e.g. a fossil (or photo of a fossil) of a trilobite or sea snail. Ask students what they think it is. Can they guess what they will be learning about in this unit?

Ideas for plenaries

Plan plenaries for strategic points throughout the lesson, as well as at the end.

Mid-lesson

1 Students create an attention-grabbing headline for a news report about the asteroid collision 66 million years ago which caused the extinction of the dinosaurs.

2 Why did the fish walk? Use the 'Why? Why? Why?' technique of asking repeated questions to get deeper into the subject of why fish left the oceans and evolved to live on the land.

3 Can students explain the difference between a rock and a fossil? Ideally you could show an example of each to the class. Both provide clues to the past.

End-of-lesson

4 What if an asteroid hadn't wiped out the dinosaurs 66 million years ago? Discuss.

Is it all a matter of luck? Would we be here if the dinosaurs hadn't been wiped out? (Each mass extinction removes potential evolutionary pathways, but leaves room for other species to flourish and evolve. And how does that fit with God?)

5 Do 'Your turn' question 7 as a plenary.

6 Traffic lights: Every student has a red, amber, and green card. They hold up the colour that describes their level of confidence in relation to questions:

– Could you say where life on Earth began? (Answer: the oceans)

– Could you identify a cause of a mass extinction on Earth? (Answer: ice age, huge volcanic eruption, asteroid collision)

– Could you say where on Earth humans first walked? (Answer: East Africa)

Further class and homework opportunities

Suggestions 7–9 on page 36 of this book

geog.1 workbook, page 6

geog.1 Kerboodle: see lesson presentation, worksheets, end-of-lesson assessment

Answers to 'Your turn'

1 The unjumbled words are:
a cells **b** evolve **c** species **d** dinosaurs **e** mammals

2 mammal

3 a About 164 million years.

b A huge asteroid (about 10 km across) struck Earth. It struck in the Yucatán Peninsula in Mexico. Shockwaves reverberated around Earth, blasting everything in their way. The impact threw up dust that blocked out the Sun, and molten rock that caused fires. (Note: many experts think the dinosaurs were already under threat from climate change, caused by volcanic eruptions, and that the asteroid was the last straw.)

4 a About 200 000 million years ago.

b In East Africa; scientists have traced our DNA to Ethiopia.

5 An episode about 248 million years ago, in which a great many species were killed off: over three-quarters of all species. We think the cause was a massive eruption of lava in Siberia. (Note that there are other theories too, and many factors may have contributed.)

6 Students can decide first on the reason for the mass extinction, to make the exercise easier. For example: rapid global warming, impact by another asteroid, a huge volcanic eruption, nuclear warfare on Earth, attack from another planet in another solar system. Encourage them to decide which species are affected. Mainly plants? Mainly marine life? Mammals only? Or everything?

7 This question will be challenging for most students. They might want to think about the effects on our bodies and brains over many many generations of things like: living mostly indoors; too little exercise; looking at very small screens; using digital technology; a warming Earth; and so on. Might we all have the same skin colour by then? Might we have adapted to living on another planet?

Note that studies are already picking up some slow evolutionary changes. (For example, a study in Framingham in the USA showed that the average woman was very slowly becoming shorter and plumper.)

Could a new human species already be developing somewhere? (Remember, we overlapped with the Neanderthals.)

Earth's story: the timescale

help at a glance

About this unit

This unit introduces the geological timescale, which sums up what has been learned about Earth, and life on Earth, from rocks and fossils.

Key points

- Scientists have learned a great deal about Earth's history by studying rocks and fossils, over hundreds of years.

- What they learned has been summarised to give us the geological timescale.

- In this timescale, Earth's 4.5 billion years is divided into blocks of time.

- The largest blocks are eons. These are divided into eras, which are in turn divided into periods. (Note that on page 11 of the students' book, subdivisions of the Precambrian eon are not shown, for simplicity.)

- The Precambrian eon covers an enormous span of time, almost 4 billion years. (It is a super eon.) During that time, simple cells evolved, and the first soft-bodied animals appeared. But then came an explosion of life, which marks the start of a new eon.

- Many of the periods are named after places where rocks were studied, or tribes who have lived in those places. Many of the names come from Latin words.

- Several periods ended with a mass extinction or a change in climate, which affected evolution in the next period. Species that were wiped out could no longer evolve – and other species were able to flourish in their absence.

Key vocabulary

geological timescale, Precambrian eon, era, period, Cambrian period, Carboniferous period, Cretaceous period

Skills practised in 'Your turn'

- Geography skills: q1, q2, q4, q7, interpret a table of information

- Literacy skills: q2, define; q8, write for a specific audience

- Thinking skills: q3, q9, come up with reasons and explanations; q6, match names to descriptions

Unit outcomes

By the end of this unit most students should be able to:

- explain the terms given in 'Key vocabulary' above

- in particular, explain what the geological timescale is

- state how long the Precambrian eon lasted, and say what kinds of life existed then

- give one fact about each of these periods: the Carboniferous, Permian, Jurassic, and Quaternary

Ideas for a starter

1. Recap: Write a selection of jumbled words from Unit 1.2 on the board. Students unjumble, and define / explain.

2. Ask: How many zeros are there in the number 'one billion'? (Answer: 9) Earth is about 4.5 billion years old. Can students write that out as a number?

3. Kick-off: The school timetable covers a one- (or two-) week timescale and shows which lessons happen when. Earth's timescale covers 4.5 billion years. Ask: If you made a timetable for Earth, what key things would you want to record on it?

Ideas for plenaries

Plan plenaries for strategic points throughout the lesson, as well as at the end.

Mid-lesson

1 Ask: What does *Carboniferous* mean? (Answer: coal bearing.) Imagine you have travelled back in time to the Carboniferous period. What can you see around you? (Answer: lush forests, reptiles, giant insects.) How far back in time have you travelled? (Answer: 290–200 million years.)

2 Do 'Your turn' question 3 as a plenary.

3 Explore the geological timescale. For example, ask: In which geological eras did these species first appear on Earth?

   a algae   **b** birds   **c** trees with cones

   d elephants   **e** insects   **f** *Homo sapiens* (us)

   Put them in order of appearance on Earth, oldest first. (Answer: a, e, c, b, d, f)

4 Write these headings on the whiteboard: *Carboniferous period*, *Permian period*, *Jurassic period*, and *Quaternary period*. Ask students for facts about each one.

End-of-lesson

5 Give me five! Summarise today's lesson in five points, five words in each.

6 Write words on the whiteboard, and ask students what they think they mean, or do a 'heads and tails' activity. (eon = an indefinitely long period of time; paleo = ancient; meso = middle; ceto = recent; zoic = animal life)

7 Ask: What if there had been no mass extinctions?

Further class and homework opportunities

Suggestions 10–15 on page 36 of this book

geog.1 workbook, page 7

geog.1 Kerboodle: see lesson presentation, worksheets, end-of-lesson assessment

Answers to 'Your turn'

1 Top

2 **a** A very long time; the biggest block of time in the geological timescale

   b Almost 4 billion years

   c Simple single cells; more complex cells; and eventually, towards the end of the eon, soft-bodied animals such as sponges, worms, and jellyfish.

3 It was a very long time ago, and Earth's surface has undergone many changes, including rock being worn away by erosion, and new layers of rock formed. So fossils may have been destroyed, or covered up forever. The living things were also small, making fossils harder to spot. In addition, soft-bodied animals would leave only traces. (Shells and bones are easier to fossilise.)

4 **a** Mesozoic   **b** Cenozoic   **c** Quaternary

5 Coal

6 **a** Cambrian   **b** Devonian   **c** Permian
   d Jurassic   **e** Ordocivian

7 **a** A mass extinction, probably due to a volcanic eruption

   b A mass extinction, due to asteroid impact

8 This will be a big challenge for some students, but will help them to get to grips with the geological timescale. They should mention at least that: it shows all the time since Earth began, 4.5 billion years ago; it is called 'geological' because it is based on what we learned from geology (the study of rocks), and fossils in rocks: the shortest blocks are called periods; new species appeared in every period; many periods end with a mass extinction.

9 During a mass extinction, many species are wiped out forever. There have been many in Earth's history. In the Permian mass extinction, for example, more than three-quarters of species were killed off. In addition, species are continually being killed off by other species, including us. We have hunted many to extinction, and wiped out others by destroying their habitats.

Our time on Earth

help at a glance

About this unit

In this unit, Earth's age is represented as 12 hours on a clock, to show how short a time we've been here; our migration from East Africa is then described.

Key points

◆ For most of Earth's history, the only form of life was single cells. (They are still very common today – for example, bacteria.)

◆ We humans (*Homo sapiens*) turned up 200 000 years ago. If Earth's age is represented by 12 hours, that was just 2 seconds ago.

◆ We began to leave East Africa about 60 000 years ago.

◆ At that time, Earth was experiencing an ice age; and because of all the water locked up in ice, the water levels in the oceans were low.

◆ So we were able to use land bridges – land exposed at low water levels – to cross to places normally separated by water.

◆ We reached Britain about 40 000 years ago. We left again because it got too cold. (An ice sheet was advancing.) We started to return here about 12 000 years ago.

Key vocabulary

ice age, land bridge

Skills practised in 'Your turn'

◆ Geography skills: q1, interpret a diagram; q3, q4, q5, interpret maps

◆ Numeracy skills: q1, q3, interpret numerical information on a diagram and map

◆ Literacy skills: q4, define; q6, write creatively about arriving in Britain 40 000 years ago

◆ Thinking skills: q2, come up with a list of important things humans have achieved

Unit outcomes

By the end of this unit most students should be able to:

◆ explain the terms given in 'Key vocabulary' above

◆ say that we humans (*Homo sapiens*) arrived on Earth very recently in Earth's history – only 200 000 years ago

◆ say that we started migrating from East Africa around 60 000 years ago

◆ explain why we could walk to Britain, from elsewhere in Europe, around 40 000 years ago

◆ explain when and why we then left Britain, and when we returned

Ideas for a starter

1 Recap: With books closed, divide the class into three teams: Paleozoic, Mesozoic, and Cenozoic. Each team has 1 minute to give any facts it can remember about its era. If correct, the team scores 1 point. When all the teams have had their time, anyone can score extra points for a team by stating new correct facts for any era.

2 Kick-start: All about time: Who is the first to answer these questions correctly?

How many seconds are there in 1 hour? (3600). How many in 12 hours? (43 200)

Hands up anyone who arrived for school today with seconds to spare!

Ideas for plenaries

Plan plenaries at strategic points throughout the lesson, as well as at the end.

Mid-lesson

1 Ask: When did people first arrive in Britain? How did they get there? How long did it take them to migrate there from the continent of Africa?

2 Ask: If you wanted to travel from the UK to North America today, what different forms of transport could you take? How long would it take you? Could you walk there? Why / Why not? If you had been travelling 16 000 years ago your answers would have been quite different! Why? (Answer: You could walk from the UK to North America across 'land bridges' that were exposed during the ice age.)

3 Ask students to sum up what they have learned so far this lesson in 140 characters (a tweet).

End-of-lesson

4 Ask: Which of these appeared first: plants, humans, animals, dinosaurs, cells?

Can you place them in order of their first appearance on Earth?

5 Recap: *Homo sapiens* appeared late on Earth, but has had a big impact! Make a list of things that helped us to make an impact (e.g. fire, tools, boats, languages, migrating).

6 Stuck in the box! Place a large cardboard (or imaginary) box on the floor at the front of the class. Select a student to stand in the box – they can only leave when they answer a question correctly about today's lesson.

Further class and homework opportunities

Suggestions 16–20 on page 36 of this book

geog.1 workbook, page 8

geog.1 Kerboodle: see lesson presentation, worksheets, end-of-lesson assessment

Answers to 'Your turn'

1 **a** In water

   b Plants (by a long way)

   c Single cells

2 Answers will vary. Students might list some of these things that we invented, discovered, or developed: the wheel, engine, printing press, radio, TV, phone, computer, plane, electricity, penicillin (and other antibiotics), writing, counting, forms of money, the law, democracy (voting to choose our leaders), refrigeration, plastics, the web.

3 **a** Forty thousand years ago

   b **i** Europe   **ii** Oceania

   c Australia

4 **a** Land exposed when water levels fall in the sea/ocean; people can walk across it

   b Bering Strait

5 **a** The land bridge at B helped us to reach Australia; we could go from island to island. But on the way, we had to cross some stretches of water by boat.

   b The land bridge at C allowed us to walk to the British Isles from France.

6 Students will need to use their imaginations. It is thought that the British Isles were cold and dry 40 000 years ago, when humans arrived. (The ice sheets did not reach their southern limit until 20 000 years ago.) We would have found conifers, and low shrubs, and grass. Animals included mammoths and hyenas. We would have survived by fishing, by hunting anything we could (including mammoths and birds), and by gathering plant foods.

Our place on Earth

About this unit

This unit looks at some of the different places people live in. It aims to help students develop their geographical imaginations, and their sense of their own place.

Key points

◆ We all have a place on the planet – and our places can be very different.

◆ In geography, it helps to be able to imagine what a place is really like to live in – and it's fun too.

◆ Our own places are special. We carry memories and images of them in our heads.

Key vocabulary

place

Skills practised in 'Your turn'

◆ Geography skills: q1, q2, gather information from photos; q3, find places on a world map; q4, draw a sketch of an imagined place

◆ Thinking skills: q2, imagine what a place is like to live in, from a photo; q4, call up mental images of a place

Unit outcomes

By the end of this unit, most students should be able to:

◆ recognise that people's places can be very different

◆ recognise that you can gather a lot of information about a place, from a photo

◆ recognise that we carry images of places in our minds

◆ begin to describe their own places

Ideas for a starter

1   Recap: Imagine that one student missed the last unit – ask for a volunteer to give a 30-second review of what the unit covered. Ask others to fill in the gaps – use prompts to remind them of the key ideas.

2   Display an interesting photo of daily life, somewhere in the world, on the whiteboard. What is going on in the photo? Where are the clues? Ask students to look at the photo with these questions in mind: What? When? Why? Where? Who? What can they learn about the photo?

3   Display an interesting photo of daily life, somewhere in the world, on the whiteboard. Hold a competition to see who can think of the best caption.

4   With books closed, display one image from the unit. Ask students to describe what they can see. (You may be able to reveal the photo little by little.) Ask: How do you think it came to be like this? Where do you think it is? What would it be like to live here?

5   With books closed, display one image from the unit. Ask students what words spring to mind when they look at the image. Make a list on the whiteboard.

6   With books closed, ask students to tell you about their place, or the local area. Invite them to make a graffiti wall with their ideas.

Ideas for plenaries

Plan plenaries at strategic points throughout the lesson, as well as at the end.

Mid-lesson

1   Look at each photo from the unit, in turn. (You could display them.) Ask students to imagine it is their place. They should write a speech bubble with their feelings about it, giving just one sentence for each photo.

2   Choose two photos from the unit. (You could display them.) Ask students to say what a person from each place would think about the other place.

3   Ask students to choose a photo to show their place, to go with this set. Ask: What will your photo show? Why? What would other people think about it?

End-of-lesson

4   People have spread over most of Earth's land. Ask: Can you name five different types of place where people live? (e.g. deserts, reed marshes, cities, tundra, islands, cities …)

5   If you could choose to live in any of the places in the photos, where would you choose and why? Where would you least like to live and why?

6   Discuss: What makes a home a good place to live in? Is it more than just where it is and what it's built of? What else is important? (e.g. you might discuss the home as a place of nurture, safety, shelter, family …)

7   Ask: Do you think it's good to look at photos of other places in geography? Explain.

8   Ask: Could photos give you the wrong idea about a place? How could you avoid that?

9   Discuss what geographers mean by 'place' and/or 'a sense of place'.

Further class and homework opportunities

Suggestions 21–24 on page 36 of this book

geog.1 workbook, page 9

geog.1 Kerboodle: see lesson presentation, worksheets, end-of-lesson assessment

Answers to 'Your turn'

1   Answers will vary. Encourage students to give their reasons.

2   Encourage students to use their imaginations for this one. It's a good way to help them develop a sense of place.

3   **a**   Iraq, in Asia

    b   Mali, in (West) Africa

    c   Siberia, in Russia, in Asia. (Some students may say that part of Russia is in Europe. But Siberia is in the Asian part.)

    d   Recife, in Brazil, in South America

    e   Tokyo, in Japan, in Asia

    f   Tonga, in Oceania. (You might need to point out that the world is round – since Tonga appears in the Pacific Ocean on the left on the world map on page 140 in the students' book.)

4   Answers will vary.

5   Discuss the reasons why they want to visit their chosen places.

Earth: a very special planet

About this unit

This unit steps back to look at Earth's place in the solar system; it then gives some data about Earth and its journey, and surveys the life it carries today.

Key points

◆ The Sun, the planets, their moons, and objects such as asteroids and comets, make up the solar system.

◆ Earth is the third planet out from the Sun.

◆ Earth circles the Sun; one full orbit takes a year and gives us the seasons.

◆ Earth spins as it travels; one full spin takes 24 hours and gives us day and night.

◆ Earth is surrounded by a layer of gas, the atmosphere.

◆ Earth carries life: over a million known species, and perhaps millions more. So far, we have not found life on any other planet.

Key vocabulary

solar system, atmosphere, air

Skills practised in 'Your turn'

◆ Geography skills: q2, q4, interpret diagrams

◆ Literacy skills: q1, define; q6, write an address (in the Universe)

◆ Thinking skills: q3, apply simple logic; q5, review facts, choose one, and explain why; q7, make a decision after assessing consequences, and give reasons

Unit outcomes

By the end of this unit most students should be able to:

◆ explain the terms given in 'Key vocabulary' above

◆ explain what the solar system is

◆ say why Earth has seasons, and day and night

◆ say that Earth has at least a million *known* species – and may have millions more still to be discovered

Ideas for a starter

1 Using Google Earth, zoom in to see some of the places shown in the previous unit.

2 Play some musical excerpts from 'The Planets' by Gustav Holst. This is one of the best-known and most-performed pieces of classical music. Ask: Which planets are represented in the music? How are they represented?

3 People have migrated to most parts of Earth, living in very different types of place, but could we live on other planets?

Take a Yes / No vote. Ask students to justify their opinion.

Ideas for plenaries

Plan plenaries at strategic points throughout the lesson, as well as at the end.

Mid-lesson

1   Ask: What is Earth made of? Why does it look blue from space?

2   Do 'Your turn' question 3 as a plenary.

3   Ask: At this moment, is it daytime or night in Australia? How do you know? (Students can look at Australia on the map on pages 140–141 of the students' book and the diagram on page 17, or you could display the images.)

4   Say: We go round the Sun once a year. Do you think this has any effect on the weather?

End-of-lesson

5   Recap: Which do you think are the three most important things you have learned about planet Earth today? Why?

6   Ask: Can you unscramble these jumbled-up words?

temsoc   rasetoid   losar ytemss   hersmopeat

Write one sentence to describe each word you have unscrambled.

7   Say: The African elephant has been around for 7 million years, but now there are only about 70 000 left. Why do you think that is? What do you think will happen to them? (You could display the photo on page 17 of the students' book.)

8   Explore the idea of millions of unknown species. Ask: Who is looking for them? Why are the unknown ones likely to be small? Why are many likely to be in ocean?

9   Explore the idea of life on other planets (anywhere in the Universe). Ask: How would you feel if living creatures were found? (Aliens, not just bacteria.)

Further class and homework opportunities

Suggestions 25–33 on page 37 of this book

geog.1 workbook, page 10

geog.1 Kerboodle: see lesson presentation, worksheets, end-of-lesson assessment

Answers to 'Your turn'

1   The solar system is made up of the Sun, the eight planets that orbit it, their moons, and other objects such as asteroids and comets.

2   a   Mercury or Venus, since it is nearer the Sun

   b   Any of the four planets beyond Earth, since they are further from the Sun

3   a   Answers will vary.

   b   They complete a full journey around the Sun each year of their lives. So they will have been around it 11 times by their 11th birthday.

4   a   No sunlight is reaching X, since it is turned away from the Sun.

   b   By 12 hours from now, Earth will have rotated through 180°, so X will be directly facing the Sun.

5   Answers will vary.

6   Students should add Europe, Earth, the solar system, the Milky Way, and the Universe, to their usual addresses. (Some might add the Northern Hemisphere.)

7   Answers will vary. Fear will be an important factor. Might it be wise to find out more about the alien beings first?

Changing Earth

About this unit

This unit introduces a key concept from the KS3 Programme of Study: that Earth's surface is being shaped and changed by both natural processes and human activities.

Key points

◆ Earth's surface is being changed by natural processes, for example, by:
   – the flow of currents of hot rock inside Earth
   – the action of rivers, waves, glaciers, and the wind, at Earth's surface
   – the action of the weather, the atmosphere, and plant roots on rocks, which break them down into soil; these processes are called weathering.

◆ These natural changes are usually very slow. But some can be fast, and dangerous. (For example, when there's an earthquake or a big flood.)

◆ Earth's surface is also being changed by human activity (farming, building, mining, cutting down forests, and so on).

◆ These changes are happening quickly, compared with most natural changes. And some are causing big problems, for us and for other species.

Key vocabulary

natural processes

Skills practised in 'Your turn'

◆ Geography skills: q2, q4, consider changes in local area

◆ Literacy skills: q3, q5, write lists, including one with bullet points

◆ Thinking skills: q1, explain and give reasons; q5, rank problems in terms of seriousness; q6, come up with responses to two fundamental questions

Unit outcomes

By the end of this unit most students should be able to:

◆ explain the term given in 'Key vocabulary' above

◆ state that Earth is being changed by both natural processes and human activities

◆ give three examples of natural processes that change Earth

◆ give three examples of changes brought about by humans

◆ give at least one example to show that natural changes can be dangerous for us

◆ give at least two examples to show that our activities cause problems

Ideas for a starter

1 Recap: True or false: Make some true / false statements relating to the last unit, for students to vote on. See who can correct the false ones. For example: Earth travels around the Sun once a day. (False – it's once a year)

2 Kick-start: Can you think of any ways in which Earth's surface is changing? Write a list on the board. See if students can group the changes under these headings: *Natural* or *Due to humans*.

3 Hold up a jar of soil. Ask: What is it? Explain that a thousand years ago it looked quite different. Can anyone say why? Then produce a piece of rock. It looked like this! Discuss the change from rock to soil as one example of natural change.

4 Keeping books closed, display the two sets of images from page 18 of the students' book. Ask students to identify the key differences between the two sets.

Ideas for plenaries

Plan plenaries at strategic points throughout the lesson, as well as at the end.

Mid-lesson

1 Ask: What natural process(es):
   - Makes mountains grow? (currents of hot soft rock flowing deep inside Earth)
   - Shape the land? (rivers, waves, glaciers, wind)
   - Breaks down rocks into soil? (weathering)

2 Ask: Why have humans cleared away the forests?

3 Ask: Do you think we humans are a 'pest'? What would mountain gorillas think?

End-of-lesson

4 Ask: Which do you think is the most dangerous change of all the changes given in this unit?

5 Ask: Which do you think has changed Earth's surface most, nature or humans?

6 Use 'Your turn' question 6 as a plenary.

7 Ask: Do you think that overall we humans are in control of our planet? Encourage students to give reasons.

Further class and homework opportunities

Suggestions 34–40 on page 37 of this book

geog.1 workbook, page 11

geog.1 Kerboodle: see lesson presentation, worksheets, end-of-lesson assessment

Answers to 'Your turn'

1 a There are many examples. Here are some:
   - The flow of hot currents inside Earth leads to earthquakes, volcanic eruptions, the building of mountain ranges, the movement and break-up of continents, and so on.
   - The flow of water, waves, ice, and wind over Earth's surface leads to landforms and features such as valleys of different shapes, waterfalls, beaches, sand dunes, canyons, and cliffs; and to flooding.
   - Weathering breaks down rock to form soil.

   b Yes. Hot currents have flowed inside Earth since it formed. Rivers, waves, glaciers, and wind flowed for billions of years before we appeared. They have been changing Earth all the time.

   c We can't control any of those natural processes. They are much more powerful than we are. So we can't prevent the changes they cause. But we can try to protect ourselves from some things, such as flooding.

   d Some examples: the weathering of rock produces soil, which we need to grow food; the shaping of the land by rivers, glaciers,

waves, and wind leads to some stunning scenery that we enjoy, and use for leisure; rivers carry silt which gives fertile soil; volcanoes throw out lava which breaks down to give fertile soil.

2 If students live near rivers or the sea, or in exposed rural areas, they may notice some natural processes at work (although these are usually very slow). But no matter where they live, weathering is going on around them. Weathering includes the effect of climate (rain, heat, frost), gases in the atmosphere, and plant roots, on all the structures around us, including buildings and bridges.

3 Students should list at least the things at the bottom of page 18 of the students' book.

4 There are likely to be some changes going on in the area, even if just roadworks, or new buildings going up.

5 Students should not copy the bullet points in the text, but write shorter ones, in their own words. The chosen order will vary. Encourage discussion.

6 Encourage discussion.

It's all geography!

help at a glance

About this unit

This unit sets out the kinds of topics students can look forward to in their KS3 geography course, under three headings: *Physical*, *Human*, and *Environmental*. It also sets out a key message for the course: geographers ask questions!

Key points

◆ Geography covers a wide and exciting range of topics. We can divide them into three areas: physical, human, and environmental geography.

◆ Physical geography is about Earth's natural features, processes, and events.

◆ Human geography is about how and where we live on Earth – how we feed, clothe, and shelter ourselves, and earn a living.

◆ Environmental geography is about how we interact with our environment. For example, about how we damage or protect places, or create pollution.

◆ Being a good geographer is like detective work: be nosy, ask questions, and look for clues.

Key vocabulary

physical geography, human geography, environmental geography

Skills practised in 'Your turn'

◆ Geography skills: q3, q4, study photos for clues; q5, q6, ask geographical questions (Who? What? Why? ...)

◆ Literacy skills: q1, complete sentences; q3, write list

◆ Thinking skills: q2, q3, match topics and reasons to an area of geography

Unit outcomes

By the end of this unit, most students should be able to:

◆ explain the terms given in 'Key vocabulary' above

◆ give examples of at least two topics for each of three strands of geography: physical, human, and environmental

◆ give at least four examples of questions they can ask about a photo or situation

Ideas for a starter

1 What is the most interesting thing you learned from the last unit, 1.7 Changing Earth?

2 Ask students to shout out topics they think are part of geography. Write them on the board. (They may need prompting for environmental topics.) Underline any that are physical geography and ask students what these have in common. Elicit a definition of physical geography. Repeat for human and environmental geography (use different colours). Students may call out some skills and resources (map reading, atlases, and globes). Put these in separate groups. You could label them *Skills* and *Resources*.

3 Write definitions of physical, human, and environmental geography on the board in big letters. Have a box for each on the table. Give each student a question on a strip of paper. Students write their names on their strips and put them in what they think are the correct boxes. Discuss the contents of the boxes.

Ideas for plenaries

Plan plenaries for strategic points throughout the lesson, as well as at the end.

Mid-lesson

1   Look at the three boxes on page 20, describing the differences between physical geography, human geography, and environmental geography. Ask: Which of these three are you most interested in, and why?

2   Ask: Why do you think it is so important to ask questions in geography?

3   Choose a person in one of the photos on page 21. Think of three questions you'd like to ask that person about being in that place. What do you think he / she would say?

End-of-lesson

4   Display an interesting photo. (It could be from Unit 1.8 or anywhere in the book.) Ask students to ask questions about what it shows. You want at least ten questions! You could do this against the clock. Then give any answers you can. How would they find answers to the other questions?

5   Draw a Venn diagram on the whiteboard with three circles – one labelled *Physical Geography*, one labelled *Human Geography*, and one *Environmental Geography*. Ask students to tell you where to write each of these areas of geography: learning about … rocks; pollution; cities; fossils; homes, rivers. Ask: Can you add any other things in the circles? Did you have any difficulty deciding what should go where?

6   Ask: Which are the two most important things you have learned today?

7   Ask: How much can you remember? Go back to page 5 and read 'The big picture' and 'Your goals for this chapter'. Can you answer any of the questions without looking at the units?

Further class and homework opportunities

Suggestions 40–44 on page 37 of this book

geog.1 workbook, page 12

geog.1 Kerboodle: see lesson presentation, worksheets, end-of-lesson assessment

Answers to 'Your turn'

1   Answers will vary – slightly, if they're correct.

2   **a** Physical **b** Human **c** Environmental
    d Human **e** Physical **f** Environmental

3   This photo was taken at the ski resort of Arosa in the Swiss Alps. *Human*: they enjoy skiing, they can afford to be here, the ski facilities are good. *Physical*: good snow for skiing at this time of year, steep slopes, fresh air, stunning scenery.

4   This photo was taken in Bangkok, Thailand, in November 2011. The Chao Phraya river, which flows through Bangkok, had flooded.

    a It shows a flooded street in a big town, or a city. People are moving through the flood in vehicles and on foot.

    b It may have rained a lot for a long period. A river may have overflowed. A dam may have burst.

    c It's natural for rivers to flood, when there is heavy rain. But people are likely to have made this flood worse. For example, by building too close to the river; by covering the soil along the river with concrete, so water can't drain away; by cutting down trees in the river basin. (Trees help to prevent floods.) People in other countries may also be responsible: scientists say we are causing global warming by burning fossil fuels; this is leading to more frequent and extreme storms and floods in many places.

5   Some questions could be: Which town or city is this? Which country is it in? When was the photo taken? How could they stop this street from flooding? Who was affected by the flood? What damage did this flood do?

6   Answers will vary.

Most of these suggestions are addressed to your students. Where research or further resources are needed, the internet will almost certainly provide the answer.

The suggestions are graded *, **, *** according to level of difficulty. Some are suitable for all levels, and can be differentiated by outcome.

Earth's story: it begins with a bang

1   **Our Sun** It gives out energy that lights up Earth and keeps us warm. What is going on inside the Sun, to produce this energy? ***

2   **Once upon a time** Make up a children's story about the Big Bang, and how it led to Earth, and us! Make it very exciting. You could illustrate it with your own drawings. */**/***

3   **How long has it got?** Stars are born, and stars die. How much longer has our Sun got? What will happen to it? Should we worry? ***

4   **You have star quality!** Yes, really. All the atoms you are built from were made by reactions inside stars. Find out more. ***

5   **Celebrate the Milky Way ...** in poetry, or song. But first, find out about it. What you learn might make you dizzy! **/***

6   **How many stars are there** ... in the Universe? **/***

Earth's story: life develops

7   **The Neanderthals** There were other species of humans before us. The Neanderthals were one. In what ways were they like us? Find out what happened to them. **/***

8   **Whatever happened to the dinosaurs?** You are a dinosaur. (Which kind? You can choose.) You have travelled to the present in an amazing time machine. Tell us what happened to you all that long long time ago. And now that you're here, you'll stay for a snack. What would you like? */**

9   **Cabbages and us** DNA is the material in our cells which controls how they develop. It is passed along as species evolve. About 40–50% of our DNA is shared with cabbages! Find out how much of our DNA we share with other species. Don't forget chimps. ***

Earth's story: the timescale

10 **Back to the Precambrian** You get a chance to try out the latest greatest time machine. You travel back to the Precambrian, with your own supply of oxygen. You emerge on a rocky plateau. You see, and hear ...? Imagine it, and tell us. **/***

11 **A memorial to extinct species** Design a memorial to extinct species. It could be made of a large dead tree branch. Or a living tree. Each student chooses an extinct species, and writes a card for it, with a drawing. Hang the cards from the tree. Is there a way to group them? Should you put the most ancient species at the bottom? **/***

12 **Display the periods ...** in the geological timescale. In a group, design a display for the periods of the geological timescale, from the Cambrian onwards. Decide what information to give about each, and in what format. For example, what was the climate like? What kinds of plants and animals were there? What marked the end of that period? Then your group will be allocated a period to research and display. There is plenty of information on the internet (for example, on the BBC's website). **/***

13 **Walk with dinosaurs** Watch extracts from a film, or a TV documentary, about dinosaurs. **/***

14 **Mary Anning, fossil hunter ...** discovered her first fossil when she was only 12. You are Mary Anning. Tell us about your life. */**/***

15 **Remember the names of the periods ...** Create a mnemonic. For example: **C**ome **O**n, **S**how **D**ad **C**arlo's **P**resent. **T**hree **J**uicy **C**rabs! **P**rice **N**ine **Q**uid! ***

Our time on Earth

16 **How long have we got?** The dinosaurs were here for a long time. Now all that is left is their fossils. What kinds of event do you think might put an end to humans? */**/***

17 **Are we everywhere?** Is there anywhere on Earth we don't live? If the answer is yes: why not? Come up with suggestions to help us live there. */**/***

18 **The Neanderthals ...** had migrated from Africa before us. Did we ever bump into them? (See suggestion 7 too.) **/***

19 **From stone to bronze to iron ...** As we migrated across the world we had only stone for tools at first. Then we discovered how to make bronze. And then, how to extract iron. How did these change our lives? ***

20 **Migrating to the moon** We migrated over Earth. Next stop: the moon. Design a small settlement for humans, on the moon. What will you need to provide? For example, is there oxygen? Everything weighs far less on the moon (one-sixth of its Earth weight). Do you need to take this into consideration? **/ ***

Our place on Earth

21 **Write a letter** Write a letter to one of the people named under the photos in Unit 1.5. Tell the person a little about your life and your place, and ask about his / hers. */**

22 **More places** Use the ideas in Unit 1.5 to build a presentation for the classroom wall. You can bring in photos of people you know, in real places, or photos from magazines or other sources. Each should have a few lines of text below, as in Unit 1.5. */**

23 **Tell me more** Find out more about one of the places or countries in the photos in Unit 1.5. Prepare a short presentation about it. */**

24 **My ideal place** Describe your ideal place to live in. (This is not about your ideal house!) Choose a geographical setting,

like in the photos in Unit 1.5, and a climate. Will it be a city? Or in the countryside? See if you can find a photo of a place that looks close to your ideal. */**

Earth: a very special planet

25 **My address, illustrated** Show your complete address, as a set of illustrations. Start with the Milky Way and work down to your front door. */**

26 **Earth from space** Look at NASA images of Earth from space. */**/***

27 **Day and night** Design a way to demonstrate why we get day and night. Use a globe and a torch if you wish. Show why people are already getting up in Australia, when we're just going to bed in the UK. */**/***

28 **The seasons** Find an animation that explains why we get seasons. A search for seasons animations on Google will provide several. You should be able to find one at the right level for your class. */**/***

29 **Man in the moon** What's the moon? Where is it? How far away? How big, compared to Earth? Find out and tell us all about it. Display images. You might create a PowerPoint presentation. */**/***

30 **ET writes home** You have arrived on planet Earth from another planet. Write a letter home, telling them what Earth is like, and why you find it very strange! */**/***

31 **Adopt a planet** Earth is just one of the Sun's planets. Choose another planet in the solar system, and tell us all about it. Where is it compared to Earth? In what ways is it like Earth? In what ways is it different? */**/***

32 **The night sky** At night, when we look up at the sky, we can see some of the other planets in our solar system. See which ones you can spot. (There are websites that tell which planets can be seen when.) */**/***

33 **Starry starry sky** What are those other twinkling things we see in the sky at night? Could they be the suns in other solar systems? Find out. Tell us. */**/***

Changing Earth

34 **Earth on the move** Hundreds of millions of years ago, the land that forms the British Isles was at the Equator! Your task is to tell the story of Britain's travels over the last 250 million years, as a long strip cartoon for the classroom wall.

This would be a very challenging group project. You'll need to give guidance about where to do research, and perhaps provide simplified material.

The result: a timeline showing where Britain was at different times relative to the Equator (guesswork!). It could also show when the dinosaurs appeared, when humans first appeared, when the British Isles split from the rest of Europe, and so on. Maps showing the break-up of the supercontinent Pangaea could be interspersed with other drawings. Each cell in the strip could have say 30–40 words of text below it. ***

35 **What happened to the mammoth?** Think of a set of Who, What, Where … questions about the demise of the woolly mammoth. And find the answers. */**/***

36 **This house would bring back mammoths** Scientists have extracted the deep-frozen remains of a mammoth, complete with blood, on an island in the Arctic. Some say there may be a way to clone it, and bring back mammoths. Should we try? Hold a debate. **/***

37 **As dead as a dodo** Where does that saying come from? Investigate. Then write the dodo's story. Add a drawing of the dodo, and a map showing where dodos used to live. */**/***

38 **A message from a mountain gorilla** The mountain gorilla on page 19 of the students' book wants you to write a message to humans, on its behalf. What will you say? (You'll have to find out first where mountain gorillas live, and why they are under threat.) */**/***

39 **Alphabet run** One way humans changed the planet was to divide it into countries. Now there are nearly 200. Do an alphabet run, with one country for each letter. (Ignore X.) Then shade in your countries and label them, on a blank map of the world. */**

40 **Global warming** There's one way Earth is changing today, which is worrying people. It's getting warmer. Is this a natural change – or are we causing it? Why should we worry? See what you can find out. */**/***

It's all geography!

41 **Swap pics** Find an interesting photo that you think is connected with physical, human, or environmental geography. Make up questions about what it shows (to which you know the answers) and write them down. Then swap photos and questions with a partner – and try to answer the questions. Award each other marks for correct answers. */**/***

42 **Crossword puzzle** Make up a crossword puzzle based on this chapter. Give it to a partner to solve. */**/***

43 **Mind map** Get a big sheet of sugar paper, and some coloured pens. Do a mind map for what you learned in this chapter. */**/***

44 **A good start?** Think about what you learned in this chapter. Has it made you interested in geography? Discuss! */**/***

2 Maps and mapping

chapter overview

About this chapter

Addressing the KS3 Programme of Study
◆ interpret a range of sources of geographical information, including maps, globes, and aerial photographs
◆ communicate geographical information through maps
◆ interpret Ordnance Survey maps including using grid references and scale, and aerial photographs

About the content
◆ The chapter starts by using maps as a way to show our connections with other places.
◆ Then it steps through maps of increasing accuracy, from mental maps to OS maps.
◆ The final unit provides background for using a globe, and world maps.

The big picture

These are the key ideas in this chapter.
◆ We are connected to people and places all over the world. We can show these connections on maps.
◆ A plan is an accurate map of a small area. It is an aerial view, drawn to scale.
◆ There are many different kinds of maps, at different levels of accuracy, from the mental maps we carry in our heads, to OS maps.
◆ Grid lines on maps helps us to find places quickly.
◆ Globes and maps of the world have special grid lines: lines of latitude and longitude.
◆ Reading maps, using map scales, making sketch maps, and using compass bearings, are basic geographical skills.

A students' version of this big picture is given in the *geog.1* students' book opener for Chapter 2, and is the basis of the interactive self-assessment form on *geog.1 Kerboodle*.

The chapter outline

Use this, and their chapter opener, to give students a mental roadmap for the chapter.

2   Making and mapping connections The chapter opener in the students' book is an important part of the chapter; see page 11 for notes about using chapter openers

2.1   Making connections How we are connected to people and places all over the world, and how this can be shown on maps

2.2   A plan of Walter's room Interpreting and drawing simple plans; drawing lines to scale

2.3   Your mental maps From the maps in our heads, to sketch maps

2.4   Real maps We move from an aerial photo to a sketch map based on it, then to a map of the same area, drawn to scale, and finally to the same map with grid lines

2.5   Using grid references How to use four- and six-figure grid references

2.6   How far? How to measure linear and non-linear distances on a map

2.7   Which direction? Using simple compass bearings to follow and give directions

2.8   Ordnance Survey maps What they are and how to use them

2.9   How high? How height is shown on an OS map (contour lines and spot heights)

2.10 Where on Earth? From the globe, with its lines of latitude and longitude, to a map of the world

Objectives and outcomes for this chapter

Objectives	Unit	Outcomes
Most students will understand:		Most students will be able to:
• that we are connected to people and places everywhere	2.1	• give examples of their own connections at local, national, and international level
• the concept of scale	2.2, 2.4, 2.5, 2.6, 2.8, 2.9	• explain what the scale on a map tells us; draw lines, using a scale; work out actual length given a line and a scale
• that they have mental maps	2.3	• explain what a mental map is; say how they can improve theirs
• what a sketch map is	2.3, 2.4	• say how a sketch map is different from other maps; draw a sketch map from a photo
• how to use grid references	2.4, 2.5, 2.6, 2.8, 2.9	• explain what grid references are; use letter / number grid references, and four- and six-figure grid references, to locate places
• how to measure distance on a map	2.6	• measure linear and non-linear distances on a map, and use the scale to work out actual distances
• how to use compass bearings	2.7	• say what the compass points are; follow and give directions, using compass bearings
• what an OS map is, and how to use one	2.8, 2.9	• explain what OS maps are; say what kinds of features they show; use an OS key; interpret contour lines and their patterns, and spot heights; use four- and six-figure grid references, for an OS map
• that the grid lines used on a globe and map of the world are lines of latitude and longitude	2.10	• point out on a globe and a map of the world the Prime Meridian and other lines of longitude, and the Equator and other key lines of latitude; explain how coordinates of latitude and longitude are used to find places

These tie in with the outcomes for each unit, in this teacher's handbook, and with 'Your goals for this chapter', in *geog.1* students' book.

Opportunities for assessment

See the formal assessment materials for this chapter on *geog.1 Kerboodle Lessons, Resources, & Assessment*. They include an extended assessment task, an exam-style question, end-of-lesson assessments, and a self-assessment form. See also the notes on pages 14–15 of this book.

Getting ready for this chapter

geog.1 Kerboodle contains plans and presentations for each unit, including interactive activities, animations, and worksheets.

About 'Your chapter starter'

The images on page 22 of *geog.1* students' book are all satellite images or photographs. They are interesting – but to find an actual place on the ground, maps are more helpful. Maps are fundamental to geography. See suggestions 1–5, on page 60 of this book, for further activities related to this chapter starter.

Mapping connections

About this unit

This unit explores how we are connected to people and places all over Earth, and how this can be shown on maps.

Key points

◆ We are connected to hundreds of people and places – in our local area, across the country, and around the world. For example, through relatives and friends, the things we buy in shops, and where we go on holiday.

◆ You can show these connections on maps.

Key vocabulary

local, national, international

Skills practised in 'Your turn'

◆ Geography skills: q1, identify places marked on a map

◆ Literacy skills: q2, use a glossary; q4, write a list

◆ Thinking skills: q2, q3, classify connections; q3, identify personal connections; q4, predict consequences if the UK were to be cut off from the rest of the world

Unit outcomes

By the end of this unit most students should be able to:

◆ explain the terms given in 'Key vocabulary' above

◆ distinguish between local, national, and international connections

◆ say that they have many connections to other places, and give examples of local, national, and international connections

Ideas for a starter

1 Throw an inflatable globe around the room. Each student makes a connection between themselves and one place on the globe, while holding the globe. The connection might be through food, travel, clothes, relatives, or books, for example. List these on the board and ask students to think of other types of links. It won't take long to build up an impressive list. Explain that we are linked to hundreds of real places and real people all over the world – even if we never go there or meet them.

2 Show some items with labels showing their country of origin – for example, a Spanish orange, a T-shirt made in China, rice from India, a British newspaper. Ask students where each item came from and who they think made it or grew it. Record this information on the board and remind them that real people were involved, to introduce the concept of interdependence.

3 Ask: Who has relatives or friends in the UK? Where in the UK? What about other countries? Start a list of connections with the heading, *Where our relatives and friends are.*

4 Ask: Where have you visited, or had a holiday, in this country? In other countries? List the places on the board, under a suitable heading.

Ideas for plenaries

Plan plenaries for strategic points throughout the lesson, as well as at the end.

Mid-lesson

1   Use 'Your turn' question 4 as a plenary.

2   Look at the map of the world on page 25 of the students' book, which shows Walter's connections from page 24. Ask: Are maps a good way to record connections? Give reasons.

End-of-lesson

3   Ask students to make, on a sheet of paper, as many connections as they can between themselves and a person in another part of the world. How many connections can they make in 5 minutes?

4   Ask: Do you think you affect people in other places, when you buy something? Give your reasons.

5   If you used Starter 2, ask students to imagine that they could travel to the country of origin of one of the items they saw at the start of the class. Ask: Where would you choose? Why? What would you like to find out about this place, while you are there?

6   Ask: Do you think being aware of all your connections will make life more interesting?

7   Ask: Do you think everyone around the world has as many connections as you? Why/Why not?

Further class and homework opportunities

Suggestions 6–10 on page 60 of this book

geog.1 workbook, page 14

geog.1 Kerboodle: see lesson presentation, worksheets, and end-of-lesson assessment

Answers to 'Your turn'

1   A = Isle of Man; B = Northumberland; C = Cornwall; D = Surrey; E = Shrewsbury; F = Nigeria; G = Japan; H = China; I = Los Angeles; J = Kenya; K = Hong Kong; L = Jamaica.

2   a   International – Nigeria, Hong Kong, Kenya, China, Japan, Los Angeles (and Jamaica)

    b   Local – Anfield, Kirkdale

    c   National – Warkworth (Northumberland), Cornwall, Isle of Man, Shrewsbury, Surrey

3   This exercise could be extended in class or for homework, taking in TV programmes and so on.

4   Students will have to think about where their food, clothing, and other goods come from, and how their lives would change if there were no internet. Encourage discussion.

A plan of Walter's room

help at a glance

About this unit

This unit aims to help students understand the concepts of aerial view, and scale, which are essential for developing mapwork skills.

Key points

◆ A plan is an aerial (bird's eye) view of a place and usually shows a small area such as a room or house.

◆ Plans are drawn accurately, to scale.

◆ The scale tells you how size on the plan relates to size in real life. You can show it as a number ratio, or using a scale line. You can also spell it out in words.

◆ Where a number ratio is written, the same units are used on each side of the ratio symbol.

Key vocabulary

plan, scale

Skills practised in 'Your turn'

◆ Geography skills: q1, q9, interpret a plan; q8, draw a plan

◆ Numeracy skills: q2, q3, q5, q7, measure lengths and use the scale to convert them to actual lengths; q4, q6, draw lines to represent lengths, using different scales

◆ Literacy skills: q10, write a set of instructions

◆ Thinking skills: q8, decide how to draw a plan; q9, explain why some items are not shown on a plan; q10, prepare instructions for drawing a plan

Unit outcomes

By the end of this unit most students should be able to:

◆ explain the terms given in 'Key vocabulary' above

◆ interpret a simple plan

◆ explain that a scale can be shown in different ways, and give examples

◆ draw lines to represent lengths, using different scales

◆ use scales to convert scaled lengths to actual lengths

Ideas for a starter

1   You have to buy carpet for this classroom. You need a drawing of the floor, to take to the carpet shop. What will you do first? Ask students to measure the length and width of the classroom floor. Show the measurements on the board. Discuss how to draw a floor plan, by scaling down the measurements. You could start with a scale of 1 : 10.

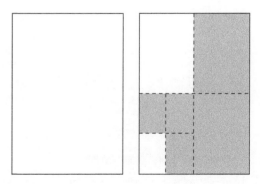

2   Confirm the idea of scale using A4 paper, as on the right. (Cut out the two smaller white shapes in advance.) Ask: How do the shapes compare? How do the lengths of the corresponding sides compare? What is the ratio (scale)?

3   Show students a variety of plans, if you can.

4   With books shut, display the plan of Walter's room. Ask: What does this show? What do you notice about it? Can you tell what size the room is in real life? How?

Ideas for plenaries

Plan plenaries for strategic points throughout the lesson, as well as at the end.

Mid-lesson

1 Ask: Which groups of people might use plans in their work?

2 Ask one student to explain how scale is used in plans.

End-of-lesson

3 Say: You work in a carpet shop. Write a set of instructions for customers about how to measure a room, so that you can estimate how much carpet they will need.

4 Ask: What height would you be if you were shrunk using a scale of 10:1?

5 Choose a student to explain to the class why scale is used.

6 Ask: Did you find it difficult working with scale? What was the difficult part?

Further class and homework opportunities

Suggestions 11–16 on page 60 of this book

geog.1 workbook, page 15

geog.1 Kerboodle: see lesson presentation, worksheets, and end-of-lesson assessment

Answers to 'Your turn'

1 X = tall white bookcase; Y = smaller black bookcase

2 300 cm (or 3 m)

3 **a** 300 cm   **b** 150 cm

4 The lengths of the lines should be: **a** 2 cm **b** 4 cm **c** 10 cm.

5 Some students will find this question difficult, since b and c involve half-centimetres, and since they must convert centimetres to metres.

  a 6 m   **b** 19.5 m   **c** 10.5 m

6 The lengths of the lines should be: 1 cm; 5 cm; 10 cm.

7

Walter's room	On the plan	In real life
How wide is it?	12 cm	360 cm
How long?	12 cm	360 cm
How long is the bed?	6.5 cm	195 cm
How wide is the big window?	5 cm	150 cm
How wide is the doorway?	2.5 cm	75 cm

8 **a** The top

  b They should draw a rectangle 1.5 cm by 2 cm.

  c It will easily fit through the doorway. You could move it end first.

9 Plans don't usually show temporary features, like books, chairs, games.

10 Below are detailed instructions. You could give these to students to follow, for drawing a plan around the school.

Drawing the plan of a room

- Collect everything you will need: a measuring tape showing centimetres, a sheet of rough paper, a pencil, a ruler, and paper to draw your final plan on. (Steel tapes are best for measuring, if you can get one. Graph paper is good for drawing a plan.)

- Draw a rough plan of the room on your rough paper, with lines and labels for all the things you will show: door, windows, and so on.

- Ask someone to help you for the next three steps.

- Clear a space around the walls, windows, and door to make measuring easier.

- Measure each wall, window, etc. in turn. Make sure to keep the measuring tape straight.

- Write the measurements on your rough plan, as you go.

- Choose a suitable scale. (Your plan can fill the whole page.)

- Using the scale, and the measurements, work out the length of each line to draw on your final plan. Write these on your rough plan, and circle them.

- Draw your final plan, using the pencil and ruler.

- Write the scale beside your plan.

- Give your plan a title.

Your mental maps

About this unit

This is a fun introduction to maps, beginning with the mental maps that students already carry in their heads. It moves from mental maps to sketch maps.

Key points

- We also have a sequence of images in our minds, like a movie, of how to get from one place to another.
- These images form our mental maps, which help us to get around. If they're good enough, we don't get lost.
- We can improve our mental maps by observing what's around us. Good mental maps help us cope with the world.
- A sketch map is a rough map that is not drawn to scale.
- Mental maps can be drawn out as sketch maps.

Key vocabulary

mental map, sketch map, map key

Skills practised in 'Your turn'

- Geography skills: q3, interpret a sketch map; q4, write directions; q5, draw a sketch map; q6, compare a sketch map and an atlas map; q7, practise observing, to improve mental maps
- Literacy skills: q1, define; q3, list
- Thinking skills: q2, identify one's own mental maps; q3, give reasons; q5, q6, make comparisons and judgements

Unit outcomes

By the end of this unit, most students should be able to:

- explain the terms given in 'Key vocabulary' above
- recognise that they already have mental maps of places
- draw a sketch map from memory of a place they know well
- say what they need to do to improve their mental maps

Ideas for a starter

1. Students draw their route to school, adding road and street names where they can. They have 5 minutes. They compare maps with a partner. What did they find easy or difficult about drawing their maps, and why? Lead to the idea of mental maps, made up from a sequence of images.

2. Ask: Tell me how to get to ... (somewhere nearby that the class knows well). Ask students how they were able to tell you. What exactly did they picture in their minds? Explain that these sequences of images are their mental maps. Repeat this exercise for a place they know less well. Why can't they give such good directions this time? Explain that we have many mental maps, and some are less complete than others.

3. Give one student the task of drawing a map of somewhere the class knows well on the board, prompted by the class. Is the result accurate? Discuss with the class why they were able to give instructions. Lead on to mental maps, the sequences of images that they carry in their heads.

Ideas for plenaries

Plan plenaries for strategic points throughout the lesson, as well as at the end.

Mid-lesson

1 Ask: In what ways is a sketch map like a map you'd buy in a shop? In what ways is it different? Which do you think is more fun?

2 Do 'Your turn' question 4 as a plenary.

3 Look at Walter's sketch map of Britain on page 29 of the students' book. Ask: How would yours be different? What else would you have to add to the key in your map?

End-of-lesson

4 Ask students to think of three differences between plans drawn to scale, and sketch maps.

5 Ask: Do you need to be good at drawing, to have good maps in your head?

6 Ask: Is it helpful to have good mental maps? Give reasons for your answer – and examples.

7 Ask: How do you build mental maps in your head? What do you think the process is?

8 Ask: How would you set about making your mental maps better? Would it be fun?

9 Ask: What has Walter included with his sketch maps? (Answer: keys) What has he put in his keys? Why do we have keys with maps?

Further class and homework opportunities

Suggestions 17–20 on pages 60–61 of this book

geog.1 workbook, page 16

geog.1 Kerboodle: see lesson presentation, worksheets, and end-of-lesson assessment

Answers to 'Your turn'

1 A map you carry in your head

2 Convince students that they have mental maps by asking them for directions to somewhere. For example, from the classroom to the school entrance or similar.

3 a Check against Walter's map.

 b They are about things that are important to him: where friends live, football, family, school, bus stop, and so on.

4 a • Go out of the front door and turn right.
 • Walk along Anfield Road until you see Arkles Lane on the left.
 • Then turn into Arkles Lane. Tim's is the fourth house on the right.

 b • Go out of the front door and turn left.
 • Walk to the end of Arkles Lane, and carry straight on, to Oakfield Road.
 • The bus stop is on the left, after the bend in the road.

 c There are two ways you could go:
 • With your back to Priory Road, turn left and walk along Walton Lane. The playground will be on your left.

 • Take the first road on the left (Anfield Road).
 • Go along Anfield Road. You will see the stadium on your right.

 Or:

 • Go along Priory Road.
 • When you reach Arkles Lane, turn right.
 • Then take the next road on your right. It is Anfield Road. The stadium is on your left.

 For 4c, you could ask students which way looks shorter on Walter's map. Can they be sure it is shorter in real life? The answer is no, since his map is not to scale. For all of question 4, point out that the success of the directions depends on how good Walter's map is.

5 c ii Our mental maps show what is important to us. So they are likely to be different for different people (and perception of distance will be different). This could be a problem if you are trying to give people clear directions.

6 Answers (judgements) will vary.

7 To see if it's working, you could ask them to repeat question 5b at a later date, and compare their new maps with their earlier efforts.

Real maps

help at a glance

About this unit

This unit should help students understand that maps show an aerial view, and that grid lines on a map are useful. We move from an aerial photo of Warkworth to a sketch map of it, then to a map drawn to scale, and finally to the same map with grid lines.

Key points

◆ An aerial photo is a view from the air. And so is a map.

◆ Sketch maps are rough maps to show what a place is like. They are not meant to be accurate, and are not drawn to scale.

◆ Sketch maps can be drawn from aerial photos.

◆ Accurate maps are drawn to scale, and the scale is marked on them.

◆ A grid superimposed on a map makes it a lot easier to say where places are.

Key vocabulary

aerial photo, sketch map, annotations, scale, grid lines, key

Skills practised in 'Your turn'

◆ Geography skills: q1, interpret an aerial photo and draw a sketch map from it; q3, compare a sketch map and a map drawn to scale; q4, find a place on a map; q5, give, and use, simple grid references

◆ Thinking skills: q2, devise a scoring system; q3, find similarities and differences; q6, assess the value of grid lines

Unit outcomes

By the end of this unit most students should be able to:

◆ explain the terms given in 'Key vocabulary' above

◆ draw a sketch map from a photo, and label and annotate it

◆ explain the difference between a sketch map and a map drawn to scale

◆ say why grid lines on a map are useful

◆ give and use simple letter / number grid references

Ideas for a starter

1 Ask for a volunteer to remind the class what a sketch map is.

2 Ask: On a map, what is the key? Why do you think it is called a key?

3 Show a map of the London Underground system. Explain that this famous map, first designed by Harry Beck in 1931, makes clever use of colours and layout to help passengers travel around the system. It does not show distances between stations, or their actual positions. Many Londoners carry this map in their heads, as a mental map!

4 Ask: Did you know that … some old maps are very valuable even though they are not accurate? Show an image of the Mappa Mundi, now in Hereford Cathedral. It was drawn on calf skin, called vellum, in around 1300. It shows what the map-maker thought the medieval world looked like. It excludes large areas of the world, such as North and South America. Ask: Why do you think that is?

Ideas for plenaries

Plan plenaries for strategic points throughout the lesson, as well as at the end.

Mid-lesson

1   Look at the photo of Warkworth on page 30 of the students' book. Ask: Why do you think they built the castle right there? Which do you think came first, a castle or a bridge?

2   Ask: What is an aerial view? See if you can draw a sketch map of your school from an aerial view. Make sure that your map has a title, a frame, and a key. Write some labels and annotations (notes) to make it clearer.

3   One student calls out the name of something on map C. (You could display it on the whiteboard.) Another has to say where it is on the map, as accurately as possible. Repeat for two more pairs of students. Then repeat for map D. It should quickly become obvious that grid lines make life easier.

End-of-lesson

4   Write the letters KLAFT in a list on the board. Ask students what the letters stand for, in relation to sketch maps. When a student answers correctly, write in the word. (Answer: K = Key, L = Labels, A = Annotations, F = Frame, T = Title)

5   Discuss: Why do geographers think maps are so great?

6   Write these in a list on the board: *aerial photo, sketch map, plan, accurate map*. Beside each item, students have to write what, and for whom, it is useful.

7   Ask: Is it easy to draw a sketch map from a photo? Can you think of anything that would make it easier? (No, not tracing paper.)

8   Ask students to identify and explain the differences between sketch maps and 'real' maps. Are sketch maps used in atlases? Why not?

Further class and homework opportunities

Suggestions 21–22 on page 61 of this book

geog.1 workbook, page 17

geog.1 Kerboodle: see lesson presentation, worksheets, and end-of-lesson assessment

Answers to 'Your turn'

3   a   Similarities: same place; river, castle, bridges, woods, and roads marked.

   b   The main differences will be in scale, level of detail, and accuracy:

   • C is to scale, so it is more accurate than a sketch map.

   • It gives more detail in terms of buildings.

   • It distinguishes between different types of roads, and shows footpaths.

   • It uses some icons and abbreviations.

   • It does not have annotations.

4   Students might notice that it's quite difficult to say where the castle is, in words. 'In the bottom half of the map' and 'in the neck of the loop' are some descriptions. Let them work through questions 5 and 6 before commenting on this.

5   a   i   B2   ii   C4

   b   i   B4: river, wood, street (road), footpath, part of church, other buildings

      ii   C3: river, part of main street, other street, footpath, buildings

6   Students should notice that the grid lines make it a lot easier to say where something is on the map, and to find things.

Using grid references

About this unit

The unit starts with an aerial photo, and a simple map of the same area, for students to compare. This helps to confirm the idea of a map as an aerial view. The map has a grid – but now the grid lines have numbers only, and they are at the lines – unlike map D in Unit 2.4. Four- and six-figure grid references are introduced, ready for OS work later.

Key points

Most of these ideas have been met already.

◆ Aerial photos and maps are closely related. Both give a bird's eye view of a place.

◆ Like plans, accurate maps are drawn to scale.

◆ Accurate maps should have a title, frame, north arrow, scale, and a key.

◆ Grid lines are also useful, to help you find things on the map quickly.

◆ A four-figure grid reference shows the square in which a place or feature lies.

◆ A six-figure grid reference gives its position within the square more accurately.

Key vocabulary

grid line, grid reference, four-figure grid reference, six-figure grid reference

Skills practised in 'Your turn'

◆ Geography skills: q1–4, q6, interpret a map, and use and give grid references; q5, compare an aerial photo and a map

◆ Thinking skills: q7, come up with a way to measure distances on a map; q8, say in what way six-figure grid references are better than four-figure

Unit outcomes

By the end of this unit most students should be able to:

◆ explain the terms given in 'Key vocabulary' above

◆ state what features an accurate map should have (scale, key, and so on)

◆ give, and use, four- and six-figure grid references to locate places

Ideas for a starter

1   Recap: What was the question? Ask students to work out the questions that go with these answers:
    –   It's a picture taken from the air.   (Q: What's an aerial photo?)
    –   It's a map drawn from a photo or picture.   (Q: What's a sketch map?)
    –   It's map drawn from pictures in your memory.   (Q: What's a mental map?)
    –   They divide maps into squares.   (Q: What are grid lines?)
    –   It lists and explains the symbols on a map.   (Q: What's a key?)

2   Whacky facts: The first aerial photo was taken from a hot air balloon over Paris in 1858. Ask: Why do you think aerial photos were not taken before that? What other places could you take an aerial photo from?

3   Look at the photo of the River Mole valley on page 32 of the students' book (or you can display it on the whiteboard). Ask: Where was it taken from? Ask students to list all the features they can spot. Students then share their lists with a partner. They then look at the map on page 32. Ask them to find all the same features on the map.

Ideas for plenaries

Plan plenaries for strategic points throughout the lesson, as well as at the end.

Mid-lesson

1   Compare the map and photo, on page 32 of the students' book. Ask: Which is better at telling you what the area is like? Why? Which would be more helpful, if you were looking for the school? Why?

2   Newsflash! On 23 December 2013 the River Mole burst its banks after heavy rain. Homes were flooded and left without electricity. The Burford Bridge Hotel (see map on page 35) was evacuated. Roads and railways were under water, so many were unable to travel home for Christmas. Ask students to write an eye-catching newspaper headline of not more than six words about this. There may be photos that you can access online.

End-of-lesson

3   Show the class a variety of maps, with grid lines. Show the students a globe, and ask what the special grid lines on it are called.

4   A grid reference has numbers that go along and numbers that go up. Can you remember which way round they are? (Answer: Walk before you climb.)

Now do 'Your turn' question 8 as a plenary.

5   In advance, draw a large grid on the board like the one on the top right of page 33 of the students' book. A metre rule may help. Label the grid lines with 2-digit numbers. Mark a scattering of 10 letters, A–J in the grids. Name a letter. When a student calls out its correct four-figure grid reference, cross it out. Each student can call out only once. Do this against the clock. If any are left when time's up, you win!

6   Repeat plenary 5 but this time for six-figure grid references. You will need to write small neat letters – or mark a dot beside each letter. When a student calls out a grid reference, ask the class to judge whether it's correct.

7   Compare the grids on map D on page 31 and the map on page 32. (You can display them on the whiteboard.) Ask: Which grid reference system is easier to use? Why? Which lets you say where something is more exactly? Why?

Further class and homework opportunities

Suggestions 28–31 on page 61 of this book (Note: these are also the suggestions for unit 2.8)

geog.1 workbook, page 18

geog.1 Kerboodle: see lesson presentation, worksheets, and end-of-lesson assessment

Answers to 'Your turn'

1   a   Any two of: Mickleham Hall, other buildings, Juniperhill Wood, other wood, fields, secondary road (B2209), small roads (drives/tracks). We can assume that the post office is in 3246, although the label is in 3245.

   b   Any two of: Mickleham village, school, pub, church, post office, other buildings, roads (A24 and B2209), river, bridge, public paths, fields.

   c   Any two of: Norbury Park (woods), river, small roads (tracks), bridge, fields. (The label for Swanworth Farm is in that square, but the farm itself is in 3146.)

   d   Any two of: A24, railway line, embankment, public paths, river, fields, one building, corners of two woods.

2   a   3045   b   3145   c   3044

3   a   A tunnel   b   A right-angle bend in a farm track
   c   A bridge over the river

4   a   324456   b   323461 (assuming it is part of the larger building)
   c   323463

5   There are trees and bushes growing along the river banks, and these show up on the photo.

6   Students need to check the photo too. You might be able to see the river through the trees, on your left, and the railway on your right. There is a public footpath to the south of you, and it might have bushes or fences along it. You might get a glimpse of Cowslip Farm.

7   It's just a little over half a kilometre (say 0.55 km), measured from the lower end of both sets of farm buildings.

8   They allow you to say more precisely where something is in a square.

About this unit

In this unit students learn how to measure the distance, both as the crow flies and by road, between two places on a map.

Key points

◆ You can find the distance between two places on a map, using a strip of paper, a pencil, and a ruler.

◆ You can find the straight line distance (as the crow flies), or the distance by road or rail.

◆ You then use the map scale to convert this to the actual distance.

Key vocabulary

straight line distance, as the crow flies, pivot

Skills practised in 'Your turn'

◆ Geography skills: q1–q3, q6, measure distance on a map; q4, q5, follow directions based on a map, including about distance; q3, q5, q6, use grid references; q6, work out directions

◆ Numeracy skills: q1–q6, use a map scale

◆ Literacy skills: q6, write directions for someone else to follow

Unit outcomes

By the end of this unit most students should be able to:

◆ explain the terms given in 'Key vocabulary' above

◆ find the actual straight line distance between places on a map, using a strip of paper, a pencil, a ruler, and the map scale

◆ measure the distance along a route, in a similar way

◆ give, and follow, directions based on a simple map

Ideas for a starter

1 Recap: Who can talk for 1 minute, without stopping, about different types of maps and their uses?

2 Ask: How would you measure the distance between X and Y (name two local places)? Students may suggest using the mileage meter on a car. How would you measure it without travelling to the two places? Any suggestions? Vote for the best one.

Ideas for plenaries

Plan plenaries for strategic points throughout the lesson, as well as at the end.

Mid-lesson

1 Ask: What is the difference between a distance measured 'as the crow flies' and one which is measured along the road? Which one is furthest, and why? Why might a pedestrian route – one you can walk along – be (a) longer, or (b) shorter than the route for cars?

2 Use 'Your turn' question 4 as a plenary.

3 Two people set out from Chapel Farm Park (2611) on the map on page 35, to go to Crabtree cottages (2512). One is riding a horse and the other is driving a car. Students discuss in pairs who they think will arrive first, and who will have travelled the shortest distance, and why. (You could display the map.)

End-of-lesson

4 Mark two heavy dots on the board, at least 60 cm apart, to represent places. Write made-up names beside them. Then write a scale on the board (e.g. *1 cm represents 1 km*).

Ask: How far apart are these places? How can you find out?

Now ask a student to measure the straight line distance between the points, using a metre rule or tape measure. The class uses the scale to convert this to the 'real' distance.

Next draw a wavy line between the dots to represent a road.

Ask: How far is it by road from one place to the other? How could you work this out? If students need prompting, hold up a piece of string and ask: Would this help?

Ask a student to measure the distance using the string. Again the class uses the scale to convert this to the 'real' distance.

5 Ask: How do you think they measure distance between places for road signs?

6 Students compare their answers for 'Your turn' question 3. Did they all have the same answer? If not, why not? Ask: What can go wrong when measuring like this? Do you think it gives an accurate result?

Further class and homework opportunities

Suggestions 23–24 on page 61 of this book

geog.1 workbook, page 19

geog.1 Kerboodle: see lesson presentation, worksheets, and end-of-lesson assessment

Answers to 'Your turn'

1 1.6 km

2 1.45 km

3 About 1.3 km

4 Chapel Farm Park

5 Crabtree Cottages

6 a Juniper Hall, 275124; St Michael's church, 273132

b The directions could go something like this: With your back to the church, turn left and walk along the road for about 0.7 km. You will see a smaller road going off on your left. Take it, and walk a little way along it – about 0.1 km. Juniper Hall is the big building on your right. (Students might notice from the photo that Juniper Hall is not a rectangular block. It has wings, which make it easy to spot on the map. The entrance shown in the photo is at the rear, away from the road.)

Which direction?

About this unit

This unit introduces the compass points N, S, E, and W, and the 'in-betweens' (NW, SW, NE, SE). 'Your turn' gives students plenty of practice in using these bearings to follow and give directions.

Key points

◆ North, South, East, and West are the four compass points.

◆ Other directions can be added between them.

◆ North west means north *of* west, south east means south *of* east, and so on.

◆ You can give and follow directions using North, South, East, and West.

Key vocabulary

compass points

Skills practised in 'Your turn'

◆ Geography skills: q1, q3, q4, give compass bearings; q2, use simple grid references; q5, q6, use a map scale; q6–q8, follow or create directions for a treasure hunt that include compass bearings

◆ Literacy skills: q8, write instructions for a treasure hunt

◆ Thinking skills: q8, design a treasure hunt based on a simple map

Unit outcomes

By the end of this unit most students should be able to:

◆ explain the term given in 'Key vocabulary' above

◆ point out the other directions (S, E, W, NE, NW, SE, SW) when told where North is

◆ follow simple directions using these compass bearings

◆ write simple directions using these bearings, for someone else to follow

Ideas for a starter

1   Show students a globe and a compass. Ask a student to point out the North Pole and South Pole on the globe. Show students the compass. Ask what it does. How does it work? Can the class work out where North is? What is the opposite of North? What other directions do you know?

2   Draw a simple compass (N, S, E, and W) on the board. Ask students what it is. Establish which way North is from the classroom.

3   Whacky facts: The compass was thought to have been invented in China, and used as far back as the 2nd century BC for fortune-telling, before it was used in navigation.

Ideas for plenaries

Plan plenaries for strategic points throughout the lesson, as well as at the end.

Mid-lesson

1   Ask: What is the opposite to North? What other directions do you know? How can you remember where West and East are on the compass? They spell 'WE'.

2   Ask a student to explain what he/she understands by the direction 'north west'? Ask another student what he/she understands by the term *south east*. (It is important to make sure they understand that north west means north **of** west.)

3   Students become living compasses. They rotate on the spot, holding out their right arms straight out in front, to point to a direction that you (or other students) call out, relative to a 'North' marker. If you want the whole class to be compasses, try this activity outside!

4   Do 'Your turn' question 8 as a plenary.

End-of-lesson

5   Ask: What kinds of problems might there be, if we did not have compasses, or the key directions N, S, E, and W?

6   Say: Some people have jobs, or hobbies, where compass bearings are really important. Think up some examples. (Pilots? sailors? Any others?)

7   In advance, ask a small team of students to make up 20 quiz questions about the map on page 139 of the students' book, using bearings. (Or do this yourself.)
    For example:
    –   Which is the most northerly city shown on the map?
    –   Name a city starting with B, directly west of London.
    –   What sea lies off the east coast of England?

    The team then asks the rest of the class these questions. The class gets 1 mark for each correct answer. The quiz team gets 1 mark for each wrong one. (Or the quiz could be against the clock.)

Further class and homework opportunities

Suggestions 25–27 on page 61 of this book

geog.1 workbook, page 20

geog.1 Kerboodle: see lesson presentation, worksheets, and end-of-lesson assessment

Answers to 'Your turn'

1	a	South	b	East	4	a	South	b	North west
	c	South west	d	North west		c	South east		
2	a	Riding school	b	Hostel	5	About 110 m			
	c	Ice cream parlour	d	Bike hire	6	He stayed in cottage 1.			
3	a	South	b	North west	7	Students should make the word 'tomato'.			

Ordnance Survey maps

help at a glance

About this unit

This unit presents the first OS map of *geog.123*. It's a fairly simple map that includes Warkworth, which also appeared in the photo on page 30 of *geog.1* students' book.

Key points

- ◆ OS maps are detailed maps of places, drawn to scale.
- ◆ OS maps are usually at scales of 1:25 000 or 1:50 000 (so 1 cm represents either 0.25 km or 0.5 km).
- ◆ OS maps use standard symbols to represent features. (See the larger OS key on page 138 of the students' book.)
- ◆ OS maps have numbered grid lines.

Key vocabulary

Ordnance Survey map, OS map, symbols

Skills practised in 'Your turn'

- ◆ Geography skills: q1–q11, interpret an OS map; q2, q3, q6, q9, use four- and six-figure grid references; q5, q6, compare an OS map with a photo
- ◆ Numeracy skills: q4, simple calculation based on an OS map scale
- ◆ Literacy skills: q11, write for a travel website
- ◆ Thinking skills: q10, look for clues about tourism, on an OS map

Unit outcomes

By the end of this unit most students should be able to:

- ◆ explain the terms given in 'Key vocabulary' above
- ◆ explain what Ordnance Survey maps are, and what kinds of features they show
- ◆ interpret OS symbols using a key
- ◆ use four- and six-figure grid references for an OS map
- ◆ gather information about a place from OS map

Ideas for a starter

1   Ask students to imagine they are map designers. Ask: How would you show these features on a map: a forest? a river? a school? a church? a bridge? a phone box? a picnic area? (A short list of items could be written on the board.) Students work with a partner to design symbols to use. They swap their symbols (no labels!) with another pair of students – and see if they can guess what the symbols show (good symbols should be easy to understand!).

2   With books closed, hold up some flash cards with OS symbols on (or draw them on the board). Ask students to guess what the symbols mean.

3   Display the OS map on page 39 of the students' book on the whiteboard, with books closed. Ask questions like: What does the large blue area represent? What about the long beige / yellow area? What is the wide blue squiggle? What are the little beige rectangles? Students guess without looking at the key on page 38.

Ideas for plenaries

Plan plenaries for strategic points throughout the lesson, as well as at the end.

Mid-lesson

1 The place in the photo on page 30 of the students' book is shown on the OS map on page 39. (You can display the photo.) Ask students to identify the place on the map. Ask: What features from the photo are shown on the map?

2 Imagine that you are on holiday in Amble with your family. Write a postcard to a friend. Tell them about the places you have visited. What else is there to see and do?

End-of-lesson

3 If you didn't use starter 2, use it as a plenary – but now students shouldn't be guessing what the symbols mean.

4 I spy with my little eye … a public phone box (or Birling golf links, or Hermitage Farm, or similar). A student calls out something he / she sees on the OS map on page 39 of the students' book. Other students must quickly give a four-figure grid reference. Have a timekeeper, and see how many things can be found in 5 minutes. Or allow only so many seconds for each one. (You could display the map on the whiteboard for this.)

5 Ask: What clues can you find on the OS map about how people in the area earn a living?

6 Ask: When might you find an OS map useful outside school? For example, would it be useful on holiday? If you were a walker or camper?

7 Use Google Earth to look at the area covered by the OS map.

Further class and homework opportunities

Suggestions 28–31 on page 61 of this book (Note: these are also the suggestions for unit 2.5)

geog.1 workbook, page 21

geog.1 Kerboodle: see lesson presentation, worksheets, and end-of-lesson assessment

Answers to 'Your turn'

1 The river is the River Coquet. It flows into the North Sea at Amble.

2 **a** 2407 **b** 2504 **c** 2705

3 **a** New Barns

b the 'parking' icon; on the map the icon is sitting over a caravan park, but the two blue lines point to the actual parking areas

c Warkworth Castle **d** Hermitage Farm

e water works **f** a lighthouse

4 1 cm represents 25 000 cm, or 250 m. So 4 cm represents 1000 m or 1 km.

5 The top of the photo is north.

6 Violet lives in the house on the corner, at approximately 248056.

7 The correct answer is **c**. The map shows that Amble has a larger built-up area; it has three or four times as many buildings as Warkworth (but not five or six times as many).

8 **a** Five (one in 2503, one on 2603, one in 2604, two in 2704)

b Four (all in 2604)

c Two (one in 2504, the other in 2704)

9 **a** Post office: 247060, or 267046.

b Club house: 255066.

c Phone box: 275043, or 234067; the leader lines point to the exact location.

d Old bridge: 247063; for 'old', students should look for ornate typeface in a label.

10 Caravan parks in 2703/2704 and 2505/2506; caravan site in 2507; parking areas in 2704, 2604, and 2506; information centre in 2604; picnic sites in 2506 and 2604, with toilets

11 Students should mention all or most of these: visit the historic sites – for example, the ruins of Warkworth castle and hermitage, the old bridge in Warkworth, and the marked rock in 2304; explore Warkworth and Amble; walk and sunbathe on the beach; swim; play golf; go sailing and fishing; walk by the river; visit the nature reserve (2704), go kart racing (2603), explore the rocks by the sea, looking in rock pools; have picnics.

How high?

About this unit

This unit is about how land height is shown on an OS map. 'Your turn' gives practice in finding heights at different places, identifying steep and flat land, and deciding whether a route goes uphill, downhill, or along flat land.

Key points

◆ OS maps use contour lines and spot heights to show how high land is, in metres above sea level.

◆ Contour lines join places at the same height above sea level.

◆ Contour lines are at regular height intervals: every 5 m on a 1 : 25 000 map, and every 10 m on a 1 : 50 000 map.

◆ The further apart the contour lines, the flatter the ground is. The closer they are, the steeper it is.

◆ A spot height is a number on the map, showing the exact height at that spot, in metres above sea level.

Key vocabulary

contour line, spot height

Skills practised in 'Your turn'

◆ Geography skills: q1, q3–q7, interpret contour lines; q8, read spot heights; q2, q4, q5, q7, q9, use grid references; q9, draw a sketch map

◆ Thinking skills: q2, q5, come up with reasons; q8, decide which direction a river is flowing in; q9, plan a route that fits a set of criteria

Unit outcomes

By the end of this unit, most students should be able to:

◆ explain the terms given in 'Key vocabulary' above

◆ use contour lines and spot heights on an OS map, to tell the height at a place

◆ interpret the pattern of contour lines to decide how flat or steep land is, and which way it slopes

Ideas for a starter

1 Ask students to imagine they are map designers. Ask: How would you show hills on a map? Students may suggest using shading. Point out that it is not very accurate. Any other suggestions?

2 Ask: Who can tell me anything about Alton Towers? What is there to do there? How many people have been there? What did you do? Can you describe the area?

Ideas for plenaries

Plan plenaries for strategic points throughout the lesson, as well as at the end.

Mid-lesson

1 Point out that the contour lines on the map on page 40 of the students' book are at height intervals of 10 m. Ask: How high is 10 m? Higher than the classroom? Higher than an electricity pole?

2 Spot the difference: compare the OS maps on pages 39 and 40 of the students' book.
   – Which of the two areas is flatter? How do you know?
   – Which map is on a bigger scale?

   Look at the contour lines on the map on page 39. Ask: At what height interval are these? Can you explain the difference? (Hint: compare the scales.)

End-of-lesson

3 Here are five answers. Ask: What do you think the five questions are?
   – The height above sea level
   – The contour lines are far apart
   – The contour lines are very close together
   – Every 10 m above sea level
   – Every 5 m above sea level

4 Say: You are out walking in the hills with a map and a compass. A mist has come down, and you can't see more than 3 m in front of you. How can your knowledge of compasses and contour lines help to get you safely home?

5 Ask: What do you think the pattern of contour lines around our school would be like?

6 Ask: How do you think OS map-makers find out the heights of places. (This could become a homework project.)

Further class and homework opportunities

Suggestions 32–33 on page 61 of this book

geog.1 workbook, page 22

geog.1 Kerboodle: see lesson presentation, worksheets, and end-of-lesson assessment

Answers to 'Your turn'

1 A = 3, B = 1, C = 2

2 a 0743   b It's beside the village of Alton.

3 a It shows that the land along that line is 200 m above sea level.
  b 190 m above sea level (the contour lines are at intervals of 10 m).

4 a 100 m   b 150 m
  c 130 m – but tracking the contour lines is difficult here so a good answer is 'around 128 m', using the spot height nearby.

5 a 0642; contour lines tightly packed. Students might also suggest 0742. The contour lines in 0539 are close, but not as close as in those two.
  b 1240 has only two contour lines passing through it. Students might suggest 1241 or 1242 – it's a close call. 1242 does have a large flat area – but also a steepish slope.

6 It appears to be quite hilly, in particular with a steep slope down to the River Churnet, and Toot Hill across the river. (Plenty of contour lines, close together.)

7 a Downhill (to the little river); note that the leader lines point to the exact locations of the phones.
  b Uphill; the road goes along flat land first, then turns and goes uphill.
  c Along flat land

8 a It appears to run along flat land – no contour lines cross it. (But there is likely to be a slight slope, since rivers run downhill.)
  b A river flows from high land to low. Judging by the spot heights, this river is flowing southwards. There is a spot height of 103 m in square 0742, 91 m in square 1041, and 87 m in square 1039.

9 This is a challenge, but students should have fun with it. They can go past Alton Towers. There's woodland, and a castle at Alton, and weirs on the Chernet, and lots of bridges. There's a lake or reservoir near Waste Farm, and old earthworks west of Alton.

Where on Earth?

About this unit

This unit introduces the globe, the Equator and Prime Meridian, and other lines of latitude and longitude. It shows how these lines are used to locate places. Then a map of the world is shown, with the other key lines of latitude marked in.

Ideally, a globe and a set of atlases will be available in class, for this topic.

Key points

◆ A globe is covered in a grid of curved lines. The horizontal lines are called lines of latitude. The others, passing through the North Pole and South Pole, are lines of longitude.

◆ There are two key lines: the Equator, at 0° latitude, and the Prime Meridian, at 0° longitude.

◆ The other lines of latitude are numbered in degrees north or south of the Equator. The other lines of longitude are numbered in degrees east or west of the prime meridian.

◆ You can use these lines to give coordinates for any place on Earth. (It is a bit like using grid references on an OS map.)

◆ You can give more precise coordinates by dividing degrees into minutes. (1° = 60′.)

◆ Earth can also be shown on a map, with lines of latitude and longitude. But there is always some distortion in projecting a sphere onto a flat plane.

◆ The index of an atlas gives the coordinates of places.

Key vocabulary

Equator, Prime Meridian, North Pole, South Pole, lines of latitude, lines of longitude, coordinates, degrees, minutes, Tropic of Cancer, Tropic of Capricorn, Arctic Circle, Antarctic Circle

Skills practised in 'Your turn'

◆ Geography skills: q2, use coordinates on a globe; q3, use coordinates on a world map

◆ Literacy skills: q1, define

Unit outcomes

By the end of this unit most students should be able to:

◆ explain the terms given in 'Key vocabulary' above

◆ point out the Equator and Prime Meridian on a globe and a map of the world

◆ point out the other key lines of latitude: Tropic of Cancer, Tropic of Capricorn, Arctic Circle, Antarctic Circle

◆ say that coordinates are like grid references, used to locate places

◆ find places on a globe or a map of the world, using coordinates

Ideas for a starter

1 With books closed, ask: How could you tell someone exactly where New York is?

2 Each student draws a slip of paper with a number on it. Say you'll call out numbers later to check what they've learned. (See plenary 6.)

Ideas for plenaries

Plan plenaries for strategic points throughout the lesson, as well as at the end.

Mid-lesson

1 Say: We are imaginary lines that meet at the North and South Poles: what are we? (Answer: lines of longitude. Tip: think of braces!)

We are imaginary lines that circle the globe, east and west, and we never meet: what are we? (Answer: lines of latitude. Tip: think of a belt!)

2 Ask: What is the Prime Meridian? Look at the countries it passes through, on the map on page 42 of the students' book. How many can you name? (Check on pages 140–141.) Now find where it crosses the Equator. Near which continent?

End-of-lesson

3 Ask students to make up a mnemonic to help remember the difference between latitude and longitude. (The famous mnemonic **R**ichard **o**f **Y**ork **g**ave **b**attle **in v**ain helps to remember the colours of the rainbow in the right order.)

4 Ask students to make a word grid of intersecting words (like the words in a crossword) that includes as many of these terms from this unit as they can: coordinates, latitude, longitude, Equator, degrees, minutes, Arctic Circle, Tropic of Capricorn, Tropic of Cancer, Antarctic Circle, North Pole, South Pole.

5 Ask: Why do you think it is useful for sailors to know their longitude and latitude? What might happen to them if they don't?

6 If you did starter 2: Call out numbers randomly from the set drawn earlier by students. Ask questions about what you covered in the lesson. For example, ask students to make up statements, based on the glove or map, to show that they understand the terms *latitude*, or *coordinates*. You could ask student X to make up a question for student Y, and so on. Have fun!

Further class and homework opportunities

Suggestions 34–38 on page 61 of this book

geog.1 workbook, page 23

geog.1 Kerboodle: see lesson presentation, worksheets, and end-of-lesson assessment

Answers to 'Your turn'

1 a An *imaginary* line around the middle of Earth; it is at 0° latitude.

b An *imaginary* line that circles Earth from pole to pole; it is at 0° longitude.

2 a i 30°N 75°E **ii** 15°S 30°E

b E

3 a i C **ii** E

b C and H

c A

d i D **ii** G

Most of these suggestions are addressed to your students. Where research or further resources are needed, the internet will almost certainly provide the answer.

The suggestions are graded *, **, *** according to level of difficulty. Some are suitable for all levels, and can be differentiated by outcome.

Note: the first five suggestions are related to the chapter opener.

Where is …?

1   **My address – illustrated!** Instead of 'Where is Walter?' do 'Where am I?' Use the ideas on the chapter opener to show your own address. You can use drawings, photos, and aerial photos if you can find them. (Try the internet?) Otherwise you could trace maps. **

2   **Whose address is it anyway?** Repeat 1 for a famous person in the UK or abroad. (For example, the President of the United States of America.) The class has to guess who it is! **

Aerial photos, satellite images, and Google Earth

3   **Find out about aerial photos** Page 22 of the students' book has an aerial photo of Liverpool. Find out how aerial photos are taken, and write 100 words about them. You could mention what kind of weather they are taken in, and who might use them, and for what. ***

4   **Find out about satellite images** Page 22 of the students' book shows satellite images of Earth from space. Where are the satellites? Who owns them? (Try an internet search for *satellites over Earth*.) ***

5   **Explore Google Earth** Google Earth uses a combination of satellite images and aerial photography. Find your place on Google Earth, and explore it. ***

Mapping connections

6   **Mapping your own connections** Make a list of at least 12 different places you are connected to, through family and friends. Mark these places on outline maps of the UK and / or the world. Beside each place write what the connection is. You could add drawings, photos, or postcards. (For this, stick your map on a larger piece of paper.) *

7   **The world in my kitchen** Check food and soft drinks labels at home, or in a shop. Write a list of at least 15 items and where they come from. Mark the places on a map, stuck on a large sheet of paper. Add a drawing of each item, or cut out images from shop catalogues. *

8   **The world in my life** Keep a diary of all the places outside the UK that touch your life over the next week. For example, places where your food, clothes, or people you meet come from, or places you see on TV. Mark them on an outline map of the world. Beside each, write what the connection is. **

9   **TV trail!** List all the places in the UK mentioned on the TV news over the next week. Find them in an atlas and mark them on a large outline map of the UK. Beside each place, say why it was mentioned. Then see if you can classify the reasons into groups. For example, *Politics* or *Sport*. Underline each place with a different colour depending on its group, and add a colour key. **

10   **Newspaper trail!** Repeat activity 9 for 25 places outside the UK, mentioned in today's newspaper. **

Plans and scales

11   **Scale plan** Measure a room at home, for example, the living room. Draw a plan to scale. Mark in any fixed items (such as doors, windows, radiators, fireplace). *

12   **Your bedroom plan** Draw an accurate plan of your bedroom, or a room you'd like have as a bedroom, on squared paper. Mark in any fitted items such as windows, doors, radiators, fitted wardrobes. Then draw in the furniture you have, or would like to have, to scale. You can colour it in. **

13   **My ideal house** A challenge! You have won a prize – a plot of land measuring 150 × 100 m, and money to build a house and garden on it. See if you can draw a plan of the house and garden you would like. It can be a bungalow. Graph paper will help. Design any symbols you need, and include a key to explain what they are. **/***

14   **You've shrunk!** You find a strange blue bottle with a label that says *Drink me*. So, being curious, you do. And suddenly you find you have shrunk, in a ratio of 10 : 1. What height are you now? What problems will this cause you? Describe a day in your life and all the problems you encounter. (Of course, you wouldn't really drink something without knowing what it was!) */**/***

15   **You've grown very large indeed!** You find a strange red bottle with a label that says *Drink me*. So, being curious, you do. And suddenly you find you have shot up in height, in a ratio of 1 : 10. What height are you now? What problems will this cause you? Describe a day in your life and all the problems you encounter. (Of course, you wouldn't really drink something without knowing what it was!) */**/***

16   **Measure up Britain** Look at Great Britain on the map on page 139 of the students' book. (Ignore the smaller British islands, like those around Scotland, for now.) About how long is this island at its longest point? Use the map scale to find out. About how wide is it at its widest point? About how wide is it at its narrowest point? Draw a rough map of the island and mark these distances on. **

Mental maps and sketch maps

17   **Britain as you know it!** We all have mental maps of places. Draw your own mental map of Great Britain (or the British Isles), and mark in where you think you live. No peeking at wall maps, or any other maps, while you do this! Next, swap maps with a partner, and compare them with an atlas map. Give each other a score. **

18   **The way to improve your mental maps is …** Look around you and observe, as you go places. But how will you know if your mental maps are improving? Work with a partner to design a mental map test for the area around the school. (And test yourselves in a few weeks.) ***

19 **Sketch map: journey home** On your next journey between school and home, look out for street names and landmarks. Then make a sketch map of the route. Mark in anything that would allow a stranger to follow the route easily. Find out how long it is, and mark this on your sketch map too. **

20 **Sketch map: treasure island** You are a pirate. You have hidden a trunk full of treasure on a desert island. Draw a sketch map to show where. Add lots of detail: shipwrecks, old anchors, palm trees, lagoons, hills, caves. Don't forget the scale (in paces) and a North arrow. Now write instructions to tell a partner how to get to the treasure. Give compass bearings, and distances in paces. Try it out on your partner. Did it work? ***

Maps and grid references

21 **A map of your local area** Find a map of the area around your school. The bigger the better! Then take photos within this area. Make a display for the classroom wall, with the map in the centre and photos around it. Link them with arrows (or thread) to their locations on the map. Add interesting annotations. (This could become an ongoing class project.) */**/***

22 **A class map collection** Cut out maps from magazines, newspapers, travel brochures. Try for as many different types of map as you can. See if you can include maps with grid lines on. Bring them into school and make a class collage of maps. Can you sort them into different groups? *

How far?

23 **A way to go ...** Get two blank maps – a world map and a British Isles map. Mark your home spot on each map. Next, find out how far you are, as the crow flies, from different places. For example, London, your nearest seaside resort, Edinburgh, Disneyland in Florida, New York, Mexico City, Hong Kong. Mark these places on your maps. Mark arrows from your home spot to them, and write the distances on. **

24 **How do they measure?** How do they measure distances between places for road signs? You could try ringing or emailing the local council to find out. Nominate one person in the class to do this. **

Which direction?

25 **Lost in the desert!** You and your camel are lost in the desert. If you keep going north you will reach the coast, and safety. But you have no compass, and no one to ask directions from. What will you do? Close your eyes and imagine what it is like there, how you feel, and how you will solve your problem. Now write a short story describing how you find your way to the coast. **

26 **Teaching directions** Design a simple compass wheel to teach children the compass bearings N, S, E, W, and the in-betweens. (It could be like a clock face made of cardboard, with two hands – or you may have a better idea.) Explain how your invention will be used. */**/***

27 **Sunrise, sunset** The sun rises in the east, and sets in the west. Why is this? Work out a way to explain it to the class, using a globe and torch. ***

Ordnance Survey maps

28 **Our grid references** Find a local OS map (1 : 25 000 is preferable) and locate your home, your school, other places that are important to you, and some local landmarks. Write down six-figure grid references for them. **

29 **Sketching from your local OS map** Choose an area from your local OS map (at least nine squares from a 1 : 50 000 map). Make a sketch map of the area to show a stranger what it is like. Add shading for high ground. Add symbols for the main features, and a key. **

30 **Design an OS game** Design a game to teach children OS symbols. */**/***

31 **Making OS maps** How do the OS map-makers make their maps? Find out, and write an introduction to OS map-making, for nine-year-olds. ***

How high?

32 **How do the OS map-makers measure height?** Find out and then explain to the class. This is a challenge! ***

33 **Mountain high** The OS map on page 40 of the students' book has hills – but no mountains! Find out the heights of the world's top ten tallest mountains, and show this data on a bar chart. Add the height of your local area, and Ben Nevis, the UK's tallest mountain, for comparison. (You can find the height of your local area by looking it up on Google Earth. It shows elevation at the bottom of the screen.) **

Latitude and longitude

34 **Capital cities** Create a table with three columns: *Country, Capital city, Latitude and longitude.* Then fill it in for 12 countries – at least one on each continent that has cities! */**/***

35 **The Equator and tropics** Why are the Equator, and the Tropics of Cancer and Capricorn where they are? It's all to do with the Sun. Find out and tell us. ***

36 **Lines of latitude and longitude** These help you say exactly where on Earth a place is. Prepare a leaflet or class presentation about them. You can use drawings or other visual aids (such as a globe). Don't forget to mention the Equator and the Prime Meridian. Give latitudes and longitudes of some places, including your nearest town or city, as examples. **/***

37 **Ask an app!** There are apps that will tell you your latitude and longitude at any time. GPS systems for cars and boats do the same. How do they know it? See if you can find out. **/***

38 **Further and further** Find out the distance around Earth from pole to pole, and around the Equator. Are both the same? If not, why not? Then find how far Earth is from the moon, and from the Sun. Show all these measurements on one diagram. ***

About this chapter

Addressing the KS3 Programme of Study

◆ Students should consolidate and extend their knowledge of the world's major countries and their physical and human features

About the content

◆ Students will have spent some time studying the UK in primary school.

◆ So most of the content in this chapter is provided to enable consolidation and catch up.

◆ However, some of the content will be new to all students.

The big picture

These are the key ideas in this chapter.

◆ 12 000 years ago, the British Isles were empty of people (because it was too cold). Since then, wave after wave of immigrants have settled here.

◆ Today the British Isles are made up of two countries, the UK and the Republic of Ireland; the UK in turn is made up of four nations.

◆ Like most countries, the UK is a country of contrasts, both physical (relief, natural features, weather) and human (for example, population density).

◆ Its physical and human features are inter-related.

◆ London is the UK's capital city, and by far its biggest city.

A students' version of this big picture is given in the *geog.1* students' book opener for Chapter 3, and is the basis of the interactive self-assessment form on *geog.1 Kerboodle*.

The chapter outline

Use this, and their chapter opener, to give students a mental roadmap for the chapter.

3 **About the UK** The chapter opener in the students' book is an important part of the chapter; see page 11 for notes about using chapter openers

3.1 **Your island home** Explores the main physical features of the British Isles

3.2 **It's a jigsaw!** The British Isles are divided into two countries; and the UK is made up of four nations, and divided into regions and sub-regions

3.3 **What's our weather like?** A weather map, some key points about our weather, and our overall temperature and rainfall patterns

3.4 **Who are we?** These once-empty islands have been peopled by immigrants

3.5 **Where do we live?** Population distribution in the UK, and, the ten largest cities

3.6 **How are we doing?** More about the human geography of the UK, and, in particular, its economy

3.7 **London, our capital city** Its location, a little history, and some statistics

Objectives and outcomes for this chapter

Objectives	Unit	Outcomes
Most students will understand:		Most students will be able to:
• that the terms *British Isles*, *Great Britain* and *United Kingdom* all mean something different	3.1	• identify the British Isles, Great Britain and the United Kingdom on an outline map
• that the UK is made up of four nations	3.2	• name England, Scotland, Wales, and Northern Ireland as the four nations that make up the UK
• that nations are divided into regions and sub-regions	3.2, 3.7	• name at least four of England's nine regions and identify them on an outline map of the regions; name at least six English counties
• that the UK has distinctive physical features, shown on maps	3.1	• name at least four upland areas, and at least four rivers, in the UK and say where they are on the map
• that there are patterns in how temperature and rainfall vary around the UK	3.3	• define weather; read a simple weather map; describe and explain the overall patterns in temperature and rainfall around the UK
• that these islands have been peopled by immigrants, and their descendants, over the last 12 000 years	3.4	• name at least five groups of people who came to the UK, including at least one recent group
• that population distribution varies across the UK, largely influenced by relief	3.5	• say which parts of the UK are most and least crowded, and give at least one reason to explain the pattern; name at least five of the UK's ten largest cities and mark them in roughly correct positions, on an outline map
• that the UK is a lively thriving country, and well off compared with most countries	3.6	• explain the term *economy*; give at least six facts about the human geography of the UK (including the economy)
• that London is the UK's capital city – mainly by virtue of its location – and by far the UK's biggest city	3.7	• point to the location of London on an outline map of Britain; describe how London started; explain why its location helped it to grow; give its approximate population today; describe its structure (City and boroughs); give at least three other facts about London

These tie in with the outcomes for each unit, in this teacher's handbook, and with 'Your goals for this chapter', in *geog.1* students' book.

Opportunities for assessment

See the formal assessment materials for this chapter on *geog.1 Kerboodle Lessons, Resources, & Assessment*. They include an extended assessment task, an exam-style question, end-of-lesson assessments, and a self-assessment form. See also the notes on pages 14–15 of this book.

Getting ready for this chapter

geog.1 Kerboodle contains plans and presentations for each unit, including interactive activities, animations, and worksheets.

About 'Your chapter starter'

The photos on page 44 of *geog.1* students' book, clockwise from top left, show: the River Thames and Westminster Bridge in London, with the Houses of Parliament; the Queen at the state opening of Parliament; a crowd at an unknown function; a dinosaur footprint in sandstone, found in a quarry in Cheshire; a road sign on the border between England and Scotland; 'Angel of the North' by sculptor Antony Gormley in Gateshead, England (not far from Newcastle and Sunderland); Ben Nevis in the Grampian Mountains in Scotland (height 1344 m). See suggestion 1 on page 78 of this book, for a further activity related to this chapter starter.

Your island home

About this unit

This unit explores the UK's main physical features, using a satellite image and maps.

Key points

◆ The British Isles consist of two main islands (and over 6000 small ones!).

◆ Relief is varied, with mountainous areas, hilly areas, hills, and flatter land.

◆ The UK has thousands of rivers of all sizes.

Key vocabulary

physical feature, mountainous

Skills practised in 'Your turn'

◆ Geography skills: q1, interpret a satellite image; q2, q3, compare two maps, to identify physical features; q4, compare a satellite image and a map; q5, study photos and match to places on a map; q7, describe the location of the British Isles

◆ Literacy skills: q7, write to describe the location of the British Isles

◆ Thinking skills: q5, look for similarities and differences; q7, think up advantages and disadvantages of living on an island

Unit outcomes

By the end of this unit most students should be able to:

◆ explain the terms given in 'Key vocabulary' above

◆ interpret a satellite image in terms of relief

◆ describe the pattern of relief in the British Isles

◆ name at least four upland areas, and at least four rivers, in the UK and say where they are on the map

Ideas for a starter

1 Show pictures of very different landscapes from the UK and around the world. Ask the class to say whether each is in the UK or not, and give reasons for their answers. If the landscape is in the UK, ask students to guess where. Why does the UK look so different in different places?

2 Ask students to agree on six small items to post in a box to someone who has not yet visited the UK. The items should help to show what the UK is like. List the six items chosen on the board. Discuss: Do they really help to describe the UK? Can you give an accurate picture with so few? Allow students to replace two items, and add four more, to give a more diverse or detailed picture of the UK.

Ideas for plenaries

Plan plenaries for strategic points throughout the lesson, as well as at the end.

Mid-lesson

1 Look at the satellite image on page 46 of the students' book. Ask: What words would you use to describe the British Isles? Students call out words. Write them on the whiteboard. Have the British Isles always been like this? Will they always be like this in the future? Does everyone agree?

2 Use 'Your turn' question 1 as a plenary.

End-of-lesson

3 Give each student a slip of blue card (for mountainous land) and green card (for flat land). Call out questions about the satellite image on page 46 of the students' book. Students hold up a card in response. For example: Which has Scotland got more of, mountainous or flat land? Which has Wales got more of? Which parts do you think get most rain, the mountainous parts or the flat parts? Which do you think get coldest? Which have more people living in them? You could confirm answers, or just say that they'll find out later in the topic.

4 Ask students to suggest some natural processes that have shaped the landscape of the British Isles. Now ask for some human processes that have shaped it. Which do you think made the biggest difference, natural or human?

5 Ask: What is the most exciting thing you learned today?

6 Show some film clips of the UK, to show its physical diversity.

7 A memory challenge. Write a list of the UK's main physical features on the board (upland areas, a selection of rivers and seas), and present the class with a challenge. Ask students to find a way to commit these features to memory, so that they will still know where they are on the map, this time next year. Students discuss ways to get images into their long-term memories, and agree to try it out for homework. You can test them for the first time at the start of the next lesson.

Further class and homework opportunities

Suggestions 2–4 on page 78 of this book

geog.1 workbook, page 25

geog.1 Kerboodle: see lesson presentation, worksheets, and end-of-lesson assessment

Answers to 'Your turn'

1 Students may need reminding that the largest island is called Great Britain, or Britain for short.

2 a The orange colour shows areas of high land.

   b a = North West Highlands; b = Grampian Mountains; c = Southern Uplands; d = Lake District; e = Pennines; f = North York Moors; g = Cambrian Mountains; h = Wicklow Mountains; i = Dartmoor; j = Antrim Mountains; k = Isle of Wight; l = Isle of Man; m = Orkney Islands; n = France; o = English Channel; p = North Sea; q = Irish Sea

3 A = Severn; B = Thames; C = Trent; D = Tyne; E = Tweed; F = Dee; G = River Great Ouse

4 The Shetland Islands

5 a Photo Y was taken at A. Photo Y shows a rugged mountainous area, matching A on the map, while X shows rolling hills.

   b Both places are in Britain, and neither is flat. But that's where similarities end. The place in X has green rolling grassy hills, and lots of trees, and signs of human habitation. (Look for the buildings in the distance.) The place in Y is bleak, rugged, rocky, and mountainous; there's some snow on the peaks, so it is cold; there is much less vegetation, and little sign of human habitation, apart from the road running through it. (There may be one or two buildings.)

6 Students may have very different ideas here. Travel and access for trade should be mentioned.

7 Students could mention: north of the Equator; between the Equator and the Arctic Circle, but closer to the Arctic Circle (so the climate is quite cool); the islands are part of the continent of Europe; they lie in the Atlantic Ocean; their nearest neighbour is France, which is separated from Britain by the English Channel.

About this unit

This unit is about the political structure of the British Isles. It shows how they are divided into two countries, how the UK is made up of four nations, and how nations are further subdivided into regions and sub-regions, with England as example.

Key points

- The British Isles are divided into two countries – the UK, and the Republic of Ireland.
- The UK consists of four nations – England, Scotland, Wales, and Northern Ireland.
- Each nation is divided into regions. (Only the nine regions of England are shown in this unit.)
- These regions are in turn divided into counties and unitary authorities. (Unitary authorities are smaller than counties, but are run as separate units because of their relatively large populations.)
- Dividing a country up into regions and smaller units makes it easier to manage.

Key vocabulary

country, nation, region, county, unitary authority

Skills practised in 'Your turn'

- Geography skills: q1, q2, use maps to build up an address which includes the region; q3, draw rough sketch maps of the British Isles, and shade in different political units
- Numeracy skills: q3, addition
- Literacy skills: q4, come up with appropriate labels for a timeline
- Thinking skills: q4, construct a timeline

Unit outcomes

By the end of this unit most students should be able to:

- explain the terms given in 'Key vocabulary' above
- name the countries that make up the British Isles, and point them out on a map
- name the nations that make up the UK
- say that the UK's nations are divided into regions
- name at least four of England's nine regions, and point them out on a map
- say that regions are further divided into counties and unitary authorities, and name at least six English counties

Ideas for a starter

1 Recap: Start with a quick revision quiz about the physical features of the UK. Ask students to label or draw in features on an outline map on the board. Then say we are now going to look at the UK in a different way: political. Look at map A on page 48 of the students' book together (or you could display it).

2 In AD 122 the Romans were ruling Britain. The Roman Emperor Hadrian built a stone wall right across the North of England, from coast to coast, and guarded by soldiers, to keep out the rebellious Brigantes tribes of Northern Britain. Parts of the wall are still standing today. Ask: How is Britain divided today?

Ideas for plenaries

Plan plenaries for strategic points throughout the lesson, as well as at the end.

Mid-lesson

1 Explain the terms *physical map* and *political map*. Students compare maps in an atlas. Can they pick out examples? What differences and similarities can they spot? Which type of map would be more useful for physical geography, and which for human geography?

2 Ask: Where am I? I'm thinking of a nation in the UK. When you think you know which one put your hands on your head! Example: I have borders with two other nations. I am divided into regions. Walter lives in here. My population is 53.5 million ... When most students have their hands on their heads, check who got the right answer. Try other examples.

End-of-lesson

3 Cut four contrasting maps of the UK into randomly shaped pieces. Students work in four teams. Give each team an envelope with randomly chosen pieces. Groups exchange pieces (one for one) with other groups one at a time. How quickly can they assemble a complete map? Is their map physical or political. How can they tell?

4 Draw a table on the board with five columns, but no headings. Write the names of some British towns or cities in the first column, some counties in the next, two administrative regions in the third, two nations in the fourth, and *UK* in the last. Ask what the headings should be. Ask for more entries for columns 1–4. (Students can use their books.)

5 Spend some time looking at each map on page 48 of the students' book. Map B: make sure they understand that Scotland, Wales, and Northern Ireland have regions too – not shown here. Map C: look at the counties. How many more can they name? Are unitary authorities bigger or smaller than counties? Explain that unitary authorities have enough people to act as separate units.

Further class and homework opportunities

Suggestions 5–10 on page 78 of this book

geog.1 workbook, page 26

geog.1 Kerboodle: see lesson presentation, worksheets, and end-of-lesson assessment

Answers to 'Your turn'

1 Students may need to find their nearest city on the map on page 139 of the students' book, and use that as a guide. A political wall map of the UK or British Isles would also be useful.

2 Students' diagrams should be similar to Walter's diagram on page 49 of the students' book.

3 b The shaded areas on the students' maps should match those on the maps in the top left box, on page 49 of the students' book.

c Populations, in millions, are: GB, 61.9; UK, 63.7; British Isles, 68.3. Areas, in sq km, are: GB, 228 300; UK, 242 500; British Isles, 312 800.

4 The drawing on the right shows a vertical timeline, for convenience. It's best if students draw a horizontal one, on a page turned sideways.

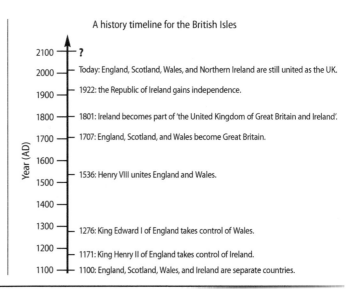

A history timeline for the British Isles

Year (AD)

- 2100 — ?
- 2000 — Today: England, Scotland, Wales, and Northern Ireland are still united as the UK.
- 1900 — 1922: the Republic of Ireland gains independence.
- 1800 — 1801: Ireland becomes part of 'the United Kingdom of Great Britain and Ireland'.
- 1700 — 1707: England, Scotland, and Wales become Great Britain.
- 1600
- 1500 — 1536: Henry VIII unites England and Wales.
- 1400
- 1300 — 1276: King Edward I of England takes control of Wales.
- 1200
- 1100 — 1171: King Henry II of England takes control of Ireland.
- 1100 — 1100: England, Scotland, Wales, and Ireland are separate countries.

About this unit

This unit is about weather patterns across the British Isles.

Key points

◆ Weather means the state of the atmosphere. For example, how warm, wet, or windy it is.

◆ The weather in the British Isles can change from day to day, and be very different in different places.

◆ But there are patterns, dictated by four factors: distance from the Equator, altitude, prevailing wind direction, and the presence of a warm ocean current.

◆ So ...

 – the south is usually warmest, since it is nearest the Equator

 – it gets cooler as you go further north, or on to higher land

 – the west coast is usually warmer than the east coast in winter, thanks to the North Atlantic Drift, a warm ocean current

 – the west coast is the wettest part of the UK; this is because the high land in the west forces the moist prevailing south west winds to rise, giving rain.

(Note that 'patterns' in fact means climate. Students will study climate in *geog.2*.)

Key vocabulary

weather, temperature, wind speed, North Atlantic Drift, windward, leeward, rain shadow, annual rainfall, prevailing wind

Skills practised in 'Your turn'

◆ Geography skills: q1, assess today's weather; q2, interpret a weather map; q4, interpret a choropleth map; q6, interpret a diagram; q7, compare maps; q8, draw a sketch map

◆ Numeracy skills: q3, assess data on a weather map, to see if it matches an overall pattern

◆ Literacy skills: q5, define

◆ Thinking skills: q3, give evidence; q5–q7, explain; q8, put labels in correct places on a sketch map

Unit outcomes

By the end of this unit most students should be able to:

◆ explain the terms given in 'Key vocabulary' above

◆ read a simple weather map

◆ point out the areas that are warmest and coolest in summer, and mildest and coldest in winter, on a map of the British Isles, and explain the patterns

◆ point out the areas that get most and least rain, on a map of the British Isles, and explain the pattern

Ideas for a starter

1 Use the BBC weather website to look up the five-day forecast for your town. Compare the forecasts for John O' Groats in the far North of Scotland and Land's End in the extreme south west of England. Students can suggest alternative places where they have friends or relatives, to look up and compare today's weather.

2 Rainfall is one aspect of the weather. Ask: What other aspects are there? Create a spider diagram of weather features on the board. Then agree a definition of weather.

3 Ask: What's the weather like today? Do you think it's the same all over the UK? Why / Why not?

Ideas for plenaries

Plan plenaries for strategic points throughout the lesson, as well as at the end.

Mid-lesson

1   Draw an outline map of the UK on the board. Ask students to come up and write *warmer*, *wetter*, *cooler*, and *drier* in the correct places, without using their books.

2   Call out a set of 15 statements about weather in the British Isles, some true and some false. Bring in knowledge from earlier lessons, with statements like: 'It rains a lot in the Cambrian mountains.' Students check the rainfall map or other information in Unit 3.3, or the map on page 139 of the students' book, then raise green or red cards.

End-of-lesson

3   Ask students to draw a weather map using symbols to show the weather on an imaginary day. They swap maps with a partner and write a brief description of the weather in words, using the information in their partner's map. They compare the two. Ask: Were you able to interpret your map correctly? How you could have made it clearer? Refer them to the weather map on page 50 of the students' book for more ideas.

4   Print terms used in this unit on to cards, for example: water vapour, rain shadow, prevailing wind, leeward side, windward side. Divide the class into two teams. Each team has 3 minutes. One team picks a card and one team member describes what is on it to their team mates without saying the specific term. When the team has guessed the answer the next player takes a card and repeats the process. After 3 minutes the second team has their turn. See who can get the most right.

5   Ask: In what ways does the weather affect our lives?

6   Ask: How would you describe the overall weather in the UK, compared with the weather in the Sahara Desert or Antarctica, for example?

Further class and homework opportunities

Suggestions 11–13 on page 78 of this book

geog.1 workbook, page 27

geog.1 Kerboodle: see lesson presentation, worksheets, and end-of-lesson assessment

Answers to 'Your turn'

1   Answers will vary from day to day!

2   Heavy cloud, rain, dull, temperature around 7 °C, wind from south west at 30 mph.

3   Yes, in general it does match. It was warmest in the south of the British Isles that day, and warmest of all on the west coast of Ireland and in the south west of Britain; it was coldest on the high land in Scotland (Grampian Mountains). But point out to students that a weather map will not match the pattern every day. The pattern shows the 'average'.

4   a D   b A   c i C   ii A

5   a   The winds that blow most often.

    b   They blow across the Atlantic Ocean, and pick up moisture from the water as they blow.

6   The high ground forces warm, moist air to rise. The water vapour cools and condenses. Clouds form, and it rains.

7   a   The west, where most of the land is high. (Ask students to compare the rainfall map with the map on page 46 of the students' book.) The moist south west winds arrive on the west coast first, and the high land forces them to rise. As the air rises it cools, so the water condenses, leading to rain.

    b   C is on very high land in the Cambrian Mountains – see pages 46 and 139 of the students' book. And it is close to the coast, where the moist south west winds arrive. So it gets a lot of rain. B is at a much lower altitude. It is sheltered by the mountains to the west. (It is on their leeward side.) By the time the winds reach B they have lost a great deal of their moisture, so B gets much less rain.

8   This shows where the four labels should go:

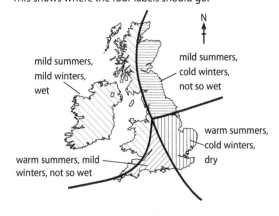

mild summers, mild winters, wet

mild summers, cold winters, not so wet

warm summers, cold winters, dry

warm summers, mild winters, not so wet

Who are we?

help at a glance

About this unit

This unit shows how all the inhabitants of the Britain Isles are descended from immigrants.

Key points

◆ An immigrant is a person who moves here from another country, to live.

◆ 20 000 years ago, nobody lived in the British Isles, because it was too cold. (We were in an ice age.)

◆ Around 12 000 years ago, as the ice sheets receded, people began to return here. And ever since, waves of people have arrived.

◆ So we are all in effect descended from immigrants.

Key vocabulary

immigrant, descended from

Skills practised in 'Your turn'

◆ Numeracy skills: q2, q3, draw and interpret a timeline

◆ Literacy skills: q1, q4, define; q2, construct labels for a timeline; q4, use a glossary and give definitions

◆ Thinking skills: q4, matching examples to definitions

Unit outcomes

By the end of this unit most students should be able to:

◆ explain the terms given in 'Key vocabulary' above

◆ explain why everyone in the British Isles is in effect descended from immigrants

◆ name at least five groups of people who came to the UK, including at least one recent group

◆ say that people have come here for a range of reasons, and give examples

Ideas for a starter

1 Ask: Who has a parent from another country? Or a grandparent? A great grandparent? A great, great grandparent? Or any ancestor? Some are bound to put their hands up. Explain that we should all have our hands up!

2 Once the British Isles was empty. Ask: Why do you think people first came here to live? Where did they migrate from? Can students remember what they learned in Unit 1.4?

3 Write a list on the board: *Celts, Romans, Saxons, Irish, Vikings, Bangladeshis, Jamaicans, Poles.* Ask students what they all have in common.

4 Write these terms on the board: *migrant, in-migrant, out-migrant.* Read a definition of the term *migrant.* Ask: Do you know any migrants? Are there any in your family? Then ask students to guess what the other two terms mean, and to give examples. Finally, connect these to the more familiar terms *immigrant* and *emigrant.* Ask whether *in-migrant* and *out-migrant* might be better terms to use.

Ideas for plenaries

Plan plenaries for strategic points throughout the lesson, as well as at the end.

Mid-lesson

1   Use 'Your turn' question 4 as a plenary.

2   Ask: Is today's topic just about geography? Does it have anything to do with other subjects? What?

3   How could you find out about your ancestors? Any ideas?

End-of-lesson

4   Ask: What if no immigrants had come to live in the UK? Describe what you think the UK would look like if it were uninhabited.

5   New arrivals bring some of their culture with them. Ask: What does *culture* mean? Ask students to draw a spider map showing elements of culture (e.g. music, language, dress, hair styles, religion, tradition, festivals, food, and architecture.) The spider map could be extended with examples, such as Norman castles, Roman laws, Indian food, or reggae music. Ask: What other cultures will you come in contact with today? In what ways?

6   Write the slogan *Celebrate our diversity* on the board. Ask: What does it mean? Do you think it would make life more exciting if everyone took that attitude?

7   Ask students which arrivals to the UK they'd like to research. Students work in small groups. Each group picks one group of arrivals to research, and makes up an enquiry question. Encourage the groups, between them, to choose a range of arrivals. The class comments on each enquiry question. Is it a well-framed and interesting question? Questions could be modified as a result. Students then carry out their enquiries as part of an ongoing class project.

Further class and homework opportunities

Suggestions 14–16 on page 78 of this book

geog.1 workbook, page 28

geog.1 Kerboodle: see lesson presentation, worksheets, and end-of-lesson assessment

Answers to 'Your turn'

1   Immigrant: a person who moves here from another country, to live.

3   **a**   Between the Normans and the Huguenots.

   b   In the 20th century.

4   **a**   See the glossary at the back of this book or the students' book.

   b   William the Conqueror, invader; Chya, refugee; Josh, emigrant from the UK (and his dad is probably an economic migrant); Joy, economic migrant – and both an emigrant from Jamaica, and an immigrant to the UK.

Where do we live?

help at a glance

About this unit

In this unit students explore a simple choropleth map of population density for the British Isles, and learn that around 20% of us live in rural areas.

Key points

◆ The population of a country is the number of people living in it. The population of the UK is around 64 million.

◆ Population density tells you how the people are distributed. It is the average number of people living in a place, per square kilometre.

◆ Population density varies across the British Isles, largely influenced by relief.
The most mountainous areas tend to have fewest people.

◆ A rural area is one that's mainly countryside – but it may have villages and small towns. Overall, the population density is low.

◆ An urban area is a built-up area, for example, a larger town or a city. The population density is high.

Key vocabulary

population, population density, rural area, urban area

Skills practised in 'Your turn'

◆ Geography skills: q2, q3, q10, interpret a choropleth map and analyse the patterns on it; q2, compare two maps; q5, match city names to locations on a map

◆ Numeracy skills: q4, display numerical data; q9, interpret a pie chart

◆ Literacy skills: q1, q6, define; q10, write a report, to include specific terms

◆ Thinking skills: q2, q9, explain; q8, identify urban and rural areas

Unit outcomes

By the end of this unit most students should be able to:

◆ explain the terms given in 'Key vocabulary' above

◆ interpret a choropleth map of population density

◆ say which parts of the UK are most and least crowded

◆ give at least one reason to explain the overall pattern of population density in the UK

◆ name at least five of the UK's ten largest cities, and locate them on a map of the UK

Ideas for a starter

1 Ask students to find out how many of the class live in the countryside, a village, a town, or a city.

2 Ask students where they'd rather live – in a city, a town, or the countryside? Why? Take a show of hands.

3 Discuss what a square kilometre is and identify an area of about a square kilometre in the local area. Establish about how many people live there. Explain that this is called the population density. Discuss whether it would be different in other areas.

4 With books closed, display the photos from page 55 of the students' book on the whiteboard. Ask: What's the biggest difference between these places? Which one is built up? Which one is an urban area? What is the opposite word, to describe the other area?

Ideas for plenaries

Plan plenaries for strategic points throughout the lesson, as well as at the end.

Mid-lesson

1   Mark out three equal areas on the classroom floor, or outside. Ask a couple of students to stand in one, a larger number in another, and a lot more in the third. Which square has the highest population? Imagine each represents 1 sq km. What is the population in each sq km? This is called the population density

2   Discuss the map on page 54 of the students' book. Explain that the deepest shade represents over 250 people per sq km. Ask: Might some places have over 500 people per sq km? Or over 1000 people per sq km? See if you can find a more detailed map to display.

3   Compare the satellite image on page 46 and the map on page 54 of the students' book. (You could display them.) Ask: What do you notice? Can you see any correlation (link) between the two? Can you explain it?

4   Write the terms *urban* and *rural* on the board and ask for local examples. Ask: Does a hamlet count as urban?

End-of-lesson

5   Give out blank outline maps of Great Britain or the British Isles. Students mark in and label the ten largest cities – they could use the map on page 139 of the students' book for help. Give them 5 minutes, working in pairs, to familiarise themselves with the locations of these cities. Then call students to the board to either label the city dots on an outline map, or insert and label them on a blank map.

6   Use Google Earth to look at urban and rural areas in different parts of the UK. What does the landscape look like now? What would it have looked like 5000 years ago?

Further class and homework opportunities

Suggestions 17–22 on page 79 of this book

geog.1 workbook, page 29

geog.1 Kerboodle: see lesson presentation, worksheets, and end-of-lesson assessment

Answers to 'Your turn'

1   The average number of people living in an area, per square kilometre.

2   a   i   50–250 people per sq km

     ii   under 50 people per sq km

     iii   over 250 people per sq km

  b   This is a mountainous area, and it's hard to earn a living here. Mountainous areas are not suitable for farming, or for many other activities. In general, people tend to settle on lower flatter land.

3   a   The UK is more crowded: over two-thirds of it has at least 50 people per sq km. Only about one-third of the Republic of Ireland has at least 50 people per sq km.

  b   England

4   Students could colour in a 100-square piece of graph paper, using a different colour for each nation: 84 squares for England, 8 for Scotland, and so on. Or create a pictogram in a similar way, with a stick figure or other icon to represent each 1% of the population. Or do a pie chart, with an angle of 3.6° for each 1% of population. Or draw a divided bar.

5   A = Manchester; B = Bristol; C = Glasgow; D = Birmingham; E = London.

6   a   A built-up area (i.e. with many buildings) such as a town or city.

  b   An area that is mainly countryside; it may have villages and small towns.

7   An urban area.

8   This could lead to a discussion of whether a small village counts as a rural area. If an area is mainly countryside, it is counted as rural, even if it has villages and small towns. The official definition of *rural* for the UK is quite complex. The amount of open space in and around a settlement is looked at (with the help of satellite images), as well as the settlement's population density. (See www.statistics.gov.uk for more.)

9   a   C is true.

  b   Students could brainstorm this from two angles:

    Why people might not want to live in the country (push factors) – too few jobs, poor services, not much to do, isolation, etc.

    Why people might be attracted to city living (pull factors) – work, entertainment, range of services, plenty of people to meet, etc.

10   This question could provide you with an opportunity for assessment.

How are we doing?

About this unit

This unit explores more of the human geography of the UK, with special reference to the economy.

Key points

◆ The UK has an ageing population, with a median age of about 40.3. That means there are more people aged over 40 than under 40.

◆ The UK's workers are employed mainly in the service sector, with many fewer in farming and manufacturing.

◆ The UK exports and imports both goods and services.

◆ The economy means all the business going on in a country. Or, to be more precise, the total production, distribution, and consumption of goods and services.

◆ Overall, the UK is thriving, and is better off than most countries. Its economy was seventh largest in the world in 2014.

◆ But there are big differences across the UK. Some areas are wealthy, and others are poor.

Key vocabulary

economy, services

Skills practised in 'Your turn'

◆ Geography skills: q10, compare and interpret photos

◆ Literacy skills: q1, comprehension; q2, q9, define; q6, write lists

◆ Thinking skills: q3–q5, come up with examples; q7, classify jobs by sector; q10, think up reasons; q11, think up more points to describe the UK

Unit outcomes

By the end of this unit most students should be able to:

◆ explain the terms given in 'Key vocabulary' above

◆ say that the UK has more people aged over 40 than under 40

◆ say that the UK attracts millions of tourists every year

◆ say that most workers in the UK are employed in providing services

◆ say that the UK's economy is doing well, overall

◆ name at least three of the UK's exports, and three of its imports

Ideas for a starter

1   Recap: True or false?

   a   Most people in the UK live in Scotland. (False. England has most people.)

   b   The population of the UK is around 64 million. (True.)

   c   Population density is the number of people who live in towns. (False. It's the average number of people per sq km.)

   d   The three biggest cites in the UK are in England. (True. Can they name them in order of population? Answer: 1 London, 2 Birmingham, 3 Leeds.)

   e   81% of the UK's population live in urban areas. (True.)

2   Put two columns on the board: *Things the UK does really well* and *Things the UK could do better*. Ask students to make suggestions for each column. Choose some ideas for discussion. What can we be proud of? What issues need to be addressed?

3   With books closed, discuss the term *economy*, then agree on a definition. Ask students to guess where the UK ranks in the world in terms of economy. Say they will find out soon!

Ideas for plenaries

Plan plenaries for strategic points throughout the lesson, as well as at the end.

Mid-lesson

1 Do 'Your turn' question 1 as a plenary.

2 What job would you like to do when you leave school? Look at the descriptions of job sectors on page 57 of the students' book. Decide which job sector it fits into.

3 Do 'Your turn' question 9 as a plenary. Discuss how it is possible to export services (e.g. premier league football matches being shown on TV around the world, British banks with branches abroad) and how the UK earns money from this.

End-of-lesson

4 Why should people visit the UK? Ask students to write a short speech to attract tourists to the UK using what they have learned in this unit and chapter.

5 The UK is a very unequal society. Some people are very wealthy, and many are hard up. Ask: If you had the means to do so, what would you change, and how?

6 Complete these sentences:

  – The most interesting thing I learned today was ...

  – The most surprising thing I learned today was ...

  – I would like to learn more about ...

  – Something I would really like to change in the UK is ...

Further class and homework opportunities

Suggestions 23–29 on page 79 of this book

geog.1 workbook, page 30

geog.1 Kerboodle: see lesson presentation, worksheets, and end-of-lesson assessment

Answers to 'Your turn'

1 Answers will vary.

2 a The period from about 1760 to 1840, when many new machines were invented in Britain, and many factories built. The Industrial Revolution then spread from here to other countries.

   b Deoxyribonucleic acid; this substance forms the genes that tell our cells how to develop.

3, 4 Answers will vary.

5 Students might include: Britain's role in the world; world-famous museums and art galleries; castles and other historic buildings; the Royal Family; British celebrities; Britain's reputation for music, literature, theatre, and fashion; shopping; London as historic capital; stunning rural areas such as the Lake District; sports events; ease of access to the UK (via ports, airports, and the Channel Tunnel). The fact that English is spoken here will attract tourists from other English-speaking countries.

6, 7 Answers will vary.

8 They are likely to find that most people on their list work in the tertiary sector (providing services).

9 a All the business activity going on in a country. If the quantity of goods and services being produced and consumed is increasing, we say the economy is growing.

   b Students may be able to think of many other exports, including of services. Be prepared to explain how and why services such as entertainment, banking, insurance, and tourism, count as exports. (For example, British music and British TV series, sold around the world, bring in money to the UK.)

   c Students may be able to think of many other imports, including of services.

10 a The place shown in X. The houses look new and well cared for, and the boats indicate an affluent area.

    b In Y, the shuttered shops look permanently shut. (Their shop signs have gone and there's a 'For sale' or 'To let' sign.) The pavement looks dirty, and the buildings look shabby.

    c A local factory (or mine, or other industry) may close down; so people lose their jobs and have less money to spend; low morale and lack of money means people don't look after the area. A tourist area such as a seaside resort may become run down because people prefer to go abroad for their holidays. There might be no jobs in a place, so people move away, and it gets less and less cared-for.

11 Encourage discussion here.

London, our capital city

About this unit

This unit presents some facts about London, the UK's capital city. In 'Your turn', students explore how and why it has grown.

Key points

◆ London is the UK's capital city, and by far its biggest city.

◆ It started as a small settlement around a bridge which the Romans built to cross the Thames, when they invaded Britain.

◆ Thanks to its location, it grew quickly as a Roman port. So they made it their capital city.

◆ London declined after the Romans left, but by the year 600 it had started growing again. It has grown almost continuously since.

◆ The City of London stands on the site of the old medieval city; it is the main financial centre of London.

◆ Greater London comprises the City of London and 32 London boroughs.

Key vocabulary

City of London, Greater London, financial centre

Skills practised in 'Your turn'

◆ Geography skills: q1, describe the location of a place; q2, interpret a map

◆ Numeracy skills: q4, q5, draw a graph of population growth and interpret it

◆ Thinking skills: q3, q6, explain; q5, make suggestions to account for data; q7, think up reasons

Unit outcomes

By the end of this unit most students should be able to:

◆ point to the location of London on an outline map of Britain

◆ describe how London started

◆ explain why its location helped London to grow

◆ describe the structure of Greater London (City and 32 boroughs)

◆ suggest reasons why London is ranked as one of the top world cities

◆ give at least three other facts about London today

Ideas for a starter

1 Ask: What do you think London's like? Where did you get your mental images of London from?

2 Mental map time: Draw an outline map of Britain on the board. With all books closed, ask five or six students to mark in where they think London is, in one colour, and their own place in another (if the school is not in London). Ask the class which dots they think are (nearest to) correct. Then they check against the map in the back of their books.

3 Students do a graffiti wall on the board around the word *London*, each writing in one thing about London. Say: Look at the things you have written. Can you see a way to group them? For example, are some about tourist attractions? Are some about entertainment? Are some opinions ones that other people might not agree with? Are some (about) facts? Are any to do with geography? Students could underline groups in different colours.

4 Using their atlases, students have 3 minutes to give you six geographical facts about London. (This will help with 'Your turn' question 1.)

Ideas for plenaries

Plan plenaries for strategic points throughout the lesson, as well as at the end.

Mid-lesson

1   Ask for a volunteer to explain what a multicultural city is, and why that description fits London.

2   In 1777, the writer Dr Samuel Johnson famously said, *'When a man is tired of London, he is tired of life'*. Ask: What do you think he meant?

End-of-lesson

3   Turn to the map on page 139 of the students' book. Ask more about London's location. For example: Would it be better nearer the sea? Why did it grow that far inland? (Could the Romans have built longer bridges?) Liverpool is on the coast, and beside a river too. What do you think helped London grow larger than Liverpool? Look at Hull. Might its location be better in any way, for our capital?

4   People have always moved to London from other places. That's the main reason its population grew. Write *pull factors* on the board. Ask students to guess what this term means. What pull factors might attract people to London today?

5   Ask: Do you think it's a good idea for you to learn something about London? Why?

Further class and homework opportunities

Suggestions 30–36 on page 79 of this book

geog.1 workbook, page 31

geog.1 Kerboodle: see lesson presentation, worksheets, and end-of-lesson assessment

Answers to 'Your turn'

1   Answers should include the terms *UK, England, south east, coast, Thames*.

2   Six counties: Essex, Hertfordshire, Buckinghamshire, Berkshire, Surrey, Kent.

3   The City of London is the old historic city, dating from medieval times and now a business and financial centre. Greater London is the city plus the 32 London boroughs.

4   The completed graph is shown below. (Providing more points to plot would give a more accurate picture, but overload students.)

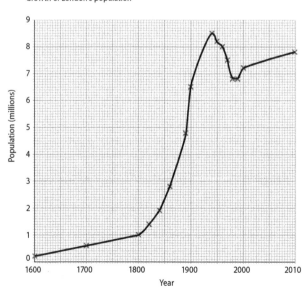

Growth of London's population

5   **a**   False. The population was larger around 1940.

   b   According to this simplified graph, it rose fastest from about 1860 to 1880 (the curve is steepest then). This was at the height of the Industrial Revolution. London had become a centre for trade and finance, at the heart of the British Empire. Its big railway stations had also been built, so it was also at the heart of a railway network linking it to the rest of Great Britain. It attracted people from rural areas, and Ireland, and the colonies.

   c   Much of the rise is due to a high birth rate, since London has a high percentage of people in the age range 20–39. Some is due to an influx of immigrants, including workers from other EU countries. People also move to London from the rest of the UK.

6   London's location near the wide mouth (estuary) of the Thames led to it becoming a major port, trading with other European countries and the rest of the world. It also meant good access to the North Sea for fishing, and waging war. Being near the coast, it is quite close to many other countries in Europe, which was (and is) good for trade. The Thames itself has historically been a source of fish, a water supply, and a means of transport. All this helped London to grow.

7   Students might mention its cosmopolitan character (wide ethnic mix). It is one of the world's top financial centres. Many big international companies have offices here. English is the international language of business. London is packed with historic buildings, museums, and galleries. It has lively theatre, music, art, fashion, and shopping scenes. It is the seat of government, and the monarchy, and home to much of the media. The climate is pleasant.

Most of these suggestions are addressed to your students. Where research or further resources are needed, the internet will almost certainly provide the answer.

The suggestions are graded *, **, *** according to level of difficulty. Some are suitable for all levels, and can be differentiated by outcome.

'Your chapter starter'

1   **Tell me what you know**   Create a spider map to summarise what you know already about the physical and human geography of the British Isles. First, set up a frame for the spider map. For example:

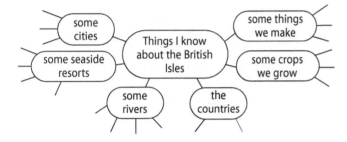

The spider map can be varied in content and extent to suit the class. Students can add to it as their work on the UK progresses.   */**/***

Your island home

2   **Write a blurb**   You have been asked to write a blurb for a new book of photography about the stunning landscapes of the UK. Make it sound really exciting – in not more than 100 words. Choose an image to go with it.   **/***

3   **Photo sketch**   Find a postcard of a place in the British Isles, showing a landscape. Draw an annotated sketch from it.   *

4   **Contrasting landscapes**   Create a wall display: a map of the British Isles surrounded by postcards and pictures from magazines, travel brochures, and other sources, showing contrasting landscapes. Use a leader line to connect each image to the corresponding place on the map.   *

It's a jigsaw!

5   **Your mental map**   Draw a mental map of the British Isles, and mark in any borders you know about, and label the seas – with no peeking at books or wall maps. (Remember your work on mental maps in Unit 2.3.) This should produce some interesting results. Agree a mark scheme. Students then use the map on page 139 of the students' book, or an atlas or wall map, to score themselves.   */**/***

6   **Polishing your mental map**   Polish your mental map of the British Isles, perhaps focusing first on the outline, seas, and borders. By the end of this topic you should be able to draw a recognisable map of the British Isles from memory. For students with less skill in drawing maps, work out a short-cut so that they can produce a simplified shape that still looks recognisable.   */**/***

7   **Know your region**   On an A4 outline map of the British Isles, mark in the countries and nations, and then just your administrative region (e.g. the South West). Add another map to show the counties / unitary authorities within the region. Mark a dot to show roughly where you live.   **

8   **Flags of the British Isles**   On an outline map of the British Isles, mark in the countries and nations of the British Isles, and their flags.   *

9   **Count the shires**   Find out how many counties in England (or the UK) end in *-shire*. Mark them on an outline map.   *

10   **A bloody battle**   The border lines on the map of the British Isles are the outcome of many struggles. Find out about one big battle between any two nations, and say what the battle was about, and describe it as if you were there. Your history teacher might help you choose a battle.   **

What's our weather like?

11   **Weather map**   Cut out a weather map from a newspaper. Mark and name a place on it (not the place where you live). Write a weather report for that place, based on the map.   *

12   **Make your own weather symbols**   Write a list of words to describe the weather: hot, windy, frosty, and so on. Make up a symbol for each word. Use your symbols to draw a weather report for the weather in your area, for each day this week. (Or one day a week, for the whole term.)   */**

13   **How good is the weather forecast?**   Draw up a table like this:

Date	Weather forecast for tomorrow	Actual weather	Weather forecast score (out of 10)

Watch a TV weather report this evening. In your table, note what it says for your area. (You can use symbols.) Tomorrow, note how the weather actually turned out, and give the weather forecast people a score out of 5. (0 = they got it all wrong, 5 = they got it exactly right.) Do this every day for a week. Work out the average score. Note: this can be a class project. Students take turns to watch the weather forecast.   **/***

Who are we?

14   **Cultural contributions**   Does your area have a Chinese restaurant? A mosque? A stall that sells West Indian foods? A pizza place? Make a list of all the local features that show the influence of other cultures. See if you can group them under suitable headings. (For example, one heading could be *Places of worship*.) The local yellow pages will help.   */**

15   **Research the invaders**   Choose a group of invaders (e.g. the Romans) and research them.   **

16   **To Britain, on foot**   People arrived in Britain 12 000 years ago. They had *walked* all the way here from elsewhere in Europe. How was that possible? Find out, and explain to the class. (Chapter 4 has clues.)   **/***

Where do we live?

17 Paper search List all the UK places mentioned in the home news or sport section of today's newspaper. Mark them on an outline map of the UK. */**

18 In the Premier League List all the UK places with a team in the Premier League at the moment. Mark them on an outline map of the UK, and write the team name beside them. */**

19 Top ten cities Tell students it's time to add cities to their mental map of the UK. Give out blank outline maps of Great Britain or the British Isles. Students mark in and label the ten largest cities, plus their own settlement if it's not one of the ten. They then familiarise themselves with the locations of these places. (For example, by covering up labels and testing themselves or getting someone else to test them.) Test students and give prizes, or let students test each other. **

20 Place quiz Choose a city (or river or island or upland area) in the UK. Without naming it, write down five facts about it, to tell the rest of the class. The class has to identify it. (This could be a game. Students take turns to present their facts. Award 1 point to the student who identifies a place first, and 1 for any unidentified place. At the end of each turn, the 'winner' marks the place on a large outline map of the UK.) **

21 Could it all be to do with coal? Students compare a map of the coal areas (from an atlas or the internet) with the population map on page 54 of the students' book. They try to explain any correlation they notice. **/***

22 Population growth Give students these population statistics for the British Isles. The population figures are in millions.

Year	Pop	Year	Pop	Year	Pop	Year	Pop
1570	4.2	1600	4.8	1630	5.6	1670	5.9
1700	6.0	1750	6.5	1801	16.3	1811	18.5
1821	21.0	1831	24.1	1841	26.9	1851	27.5
1861	29.1	1871	31.6	1881	35.0	1891	37.8
1901	41.6	1911	45.4	1921	47.1	1931	49.0
1941	?	1951	53.3	1961	55.6	1971	58.9
1981	59.8	1991	61.3	2001	62.9	2011	63.2

(The figures up to 1801, the year of the first official census, are estimates.) Students draw a line graph, and comment. **

How are we doing?

23 Population pyramid Give out a population pyramid for the UK (from the internet). Then ask some questions about it (or students make up questions for each other). **/***

24 Design a TV ad … to attract more tourists to the UK. You have to storyboard it and write down what the voice will say. */**/***

25 The Industrial Revolution … started in Britain. Tell us about it, as an electronic presentation, or as an essay with some images. **/***

26 The UK at work Do a class brainstorm of all the different types of work people do in the UK. Then allocate the jobs to a sector, and do a bar chart. (You could introduce the quaternary sector, which will be dealt with later in the course.) */**

27 The UK's food supply Which foods / food products are produced in the UK, and which must be imported? Students make up a table. It could include further divisions: *Foods from animals* and *Foods from plants*. */**

28 Where are our clothes made? Check the labels on say ten articles of clothing, at home, and list the number of items and the countries where they were made. As a class, collect the data and decide how to present it. Overall, is our clothing mostly made in the UK, or imported? Discuss reasons for any patterns. */**

29 Check the papers A student chooses a simple newspaper article about the British economy, and reads it to the class. Another student has to stand up and summarise it. ***

London, our capital city

30 London in stories London features in many novels and stories. See if you can find some examples, and read extracts that describe the city, or people's lives there, to the class. You could try *Oliver Twist*, or *David Copperfield*. Your English teacher might suggest others. **

31 Not the only capital London is the capital of the UK – and of England. The other nations of the UK have their own capitals. Draw a map of the British Isles, and mark in the national and international boundaries. Label the countries and nations, and add in and label all the capitals. Do the other capitals have parliaments too? Find out and add notes to your drawing – in your own words! */**

32 Adopt a famous building Adopt a building in London. For example, Buckingham Palace, or Tate Modern, or the Shard, or St Paul's Cathedral – or a shop. Make a card with a photo of it, and bullet points about it. Display them on the wall. */**

33 Where are those airports? There are five airports closely, or quite closely, linked to London. Which ones are they, and where are they? Mark them in and label them, on and around an outline map of London. **

34 Celebrate London Create a really fun wall display to celebrate London. *

35 A school trip to London Plan a school trip to London for your class. It could be to the Globe Theatre, for example, or the Natural History Museum, or the Thames Barrier, or wherever you like! Work out a plan for an ideal day. ***

36 Just half a minute! Students talk for 30 seconds (or a minute, if you prefer) without hesitation, repetition, or deviation, on *London: our capital city*. **/***

4 Glaciers

chapter overview

About this chapter

Addressing the KS3 Programme of Study

◆ Understand how geographical processes interact to create distinctive physical landscapes that change over time.

◆ Understand, through the use of detailed place-based exemplars, the key processes relating to glaciation.

◆ Interpret Ordnance Survey maps including using grid references and scale, thematic mapping, and aerial and satellite photographs.

About the content

◆ Starts with the last ice age, to help students understand glaciated landscapes in the UK today, and to prepare for later work on climate.

◆ Uses the Lake District as the main exemplar, through an OS map and photos. Most of the photos are taken within the OS map area.

The big picture

These are the key ideas behind this chapter.

◆ The last ice age lasted about 100000 years, ending around 10000 years ago.

◆ During that time, glaciers formed in the British Isles. They coalesced and became part of the huge glacier – an ice sheet – that covered most of northern Europe.

◆ As the ice age ended, the ice in the British Isles melted away, leaving distinctive landforms and features.

◆ We can still see them today, for example in the Lake District. These landforms and features were created by the processes of erosion, transport, and deposition.

◆ Today, there are still glaciers in Earth's coldest places. They include the ice sheets in Greenland and Antarctica, and the mountain glaciers found in many countries.

A students' version of this big picture is given in the *geog.1* students' book opener for Chapter 4, and is the basis of the interactive self-assessment form on *geog.1 Kerboodle*.

The chapter outline

Use this, and their chapter opener, to give students a mental roadmap for the chapter.

4 **Glaciers** The chapter opener in the students' book is an important part of the chapter; see page 11 for notes about using chapter openers

4.1 **Your place ... 20000 years ago!** The British Isles 20000 years ago, at the maximum extent of glaciation: mostly under ice, the rest tundra, and joined to the rest of Europe

4.2 **Glaciers: what and where?** What glaciers are, how they form, where they are found today, and a key characteristic: they flow

4.3 **Glaciers at work** How glaciers shape the landscape through the processes of erosion, transport, and deposition

4.4 **Landforms shaped by erosion – part 1** An overview of how glaciation changes a landscape; and a closer look at three landforms: the corrie, arête, and pyramidal peak

4.5 **Landforms shaped by erosion – part 2** This looks at U-shaped valleys (which may have misfit rivers and ribbon lakes); hanging valleys (which may have waterfalls)

4.6 **Landforms created by deposition** The different types of moraine, erratics, and drumlins

4.7 **Glacial landforms on an OS map** Explores an OS map for part of the Lake District, and relates the map to photos seen earlier in the chapter

4.8 **Glaciers and us** A broader look at glaciers and how they affect us; it touches very briefly on climate change, which will be covered in more detail in *geog.2*

Objectives and outcomes for this chapter

Objectives	Unit	Outcomes
Most students will understand:		Most students will be able to:
what glaciers are, and how they form	4.2	define a glacier; describe how glaciers form
that glaciers flow	4.2	explain why glaciers flow; and where they flow to
that glaciers are different sizes	4.2	explain the difference between an ice sheet and a mountain glacier
that glaciers are found in Earth's coldest places	4.2	give examples of where glaciers are found on Earth today
that Earth has experienced ice ages, when there were more glaciers	4.2, 42	explain what an ice age is; state when the last ice age started and ended, and how long it lasted
that much of the British Isles was under ice during the last ice age	4.1	describe roughly the extent of the ice sheet over the British Isles, 20 000 years ago
that glaciers shape and change the land they flow over	4.3	describe the processes of erosion, transport, and deposition by glaciers; explain what freeze-thaw weathering is, and how it affects erosion
that glaciation results in special landforms and features	4.4, 4.5, 4.6	describe the overall impact of glaciation on a mountain landscape; name and describe these and say how they were formed: corries, arêtes, pyramidal peaks, U-shaped valleys, ribbon lakes, hanging valleys, moraines, drumlins; explain where erratics came from
that we can still see glacial landforms and features in the UK today – long after the ice has gone –and identify them on OS maps	4.7	identify U-shaped valleys, ribbon lakes, misfit rivers, corries, and tarns on an OS map
that glaciers, past and present, have an impact on humans	4.8	give examples of our links with glaciers; say how global warming is affecting glaciers, and give a predicted consequence

These tie in with the outcomes for each unit, in this teacher's handbook, and with 'Your goals for this chapter', in *geog.1* students' book.

Opportunities for assessment

See the formal assessment materials for this chapter on *geog.1 Kerboodle Lessons, Resources, & Assessment*. They include an extended assessment task, an exam-style question, end-of-lesson assessments, and a self-assessment form. See also the notes on pages 14–15 of this book.

Getting ready for this chapter

geog.1 Kerboodle contains plans and presentations for each unit, including interactive activities, animations, and worksheets.

About 'Your chapter starter'

The photo on page 60 of *geog.1* students' book was taken at the snout of the Morteratsch glacier in the Swiss Alps. The figure in the blue jacket gives an idea of the scale. Note these: the caves in the melting ice; the meltwater; the material on top of the glacier, that fell from the valley sides – and which accounts for its dirty appearance; and the unsorted jumble of jagged rocks and stones which has been deposited. (Rocks and stones carried by glaciers do not knock against each other during transport, unlike for rivers. So they do not get worn smooth.)

Your place ... 20 000 years ago!

help at a glance

About this unit

This unit describes what the British Isles were like 20 000 years ago, during the last ice age, at the maximum extent of glaciation.

Key points

- The last ice age began about 110 000 years ago, and ended about 10 000 years ago. The maximum extent of glaciation was around 20 000 tears ago.

- At that point much of the British Isles was covered by an ice sheet, and the southern parts were tundra.

- Water levels in the ocean fell because water – that would otherwise return to the ocean in rivers – became locked up in ice on land. As a result, shallower parts of the ocean floor were exposed as land, joining the British Isles to the rest of Europe.

- When the ice finally melted, water levels rose again. The British Isles were once more cut off from the rest of Europe.

- People first reached the British Isles during the ice age, about 40 000 years ago. As it got colder, we left. When the ice sheet started to shrink we returned, about 12 000 years ago.

- There were animals (such as mammoth, bison, arctic fox, reindeer, antelope) in the tundra of the British Isles, 20 000 years ago. Many came here to feed in summer.

- Note that we use 'ice age', as the programme of study does, to mean the last extended cold period. But there are still ice sheets in the Arctic and Antarctic. So technically, we are still in a long ice age, that began about 2.6 million years ago.

Key vocabulary

ice age, ice sheet, tundra

Skills practised in 'Your turn'

- Geography skills: q1, define; q3, q4, interpret a map
- Numeracy skills: q1, work out how long the ice age lasted
- Literacy skills: q3, write a blog, describing a place during the ice age
- Thinking skills: q3, come up with reasons; q4, list items to take on time travel back to the ice age, and explain the choice

Unit outcomes

By the end of this unit, most students should be able to:
- explain the terms given in 'Key vocabulary' above
- state when the last ice age began, how long it lasted, and when it ended
- describe the extent of the ice sheet over the British Isles, 20 000 years ago
- explain why the British Isles were joined to the rest of Europe at that point, and how they were cut off again
- say how the ice age affected people and animals, in the British Isles

Suggestions for a starter

1   Ask: In the British Isles, is there widespread snow and ice anywhere all year round? Why not? Do you think it has always been like this?

2   With books closed, ask: What do you think the British Isles were like 20 000 years ago? Write words on the board. You can check back at the end of the lesson.

3   Brainstorm to find out what students already know about ice ages.

Suggestions for plenaries

Plan plenaries at strategic points throughout the lesson, as well as at the end.

Mid-lesson

1   Do 'Your turn' question 3 as a plenary.

2   Ask: Who can explain *why* water levels fell in the ocean, during the ice age? Draw out the facts that when snow fell it did not melt, so the rain did not run back to the ocean. In addition, lower temperatures around Earth meant a lower rate of evaporation from the ocean, so there was less precipitation.

3   Look at map B. Say: The main ice sheet did not extend to southern Europe. Why not? But there are some areas of ice in southern Europe. Why?

End-of-lesson

4   Start a big spider map on the board, with some headings in place, to summarise today's lesson. Students call out terms and phrases to add to it.

5   If you used starter 1, you can revisit the word list. Ask: Which words can be crossed out?

6   Ask: What exciting / interesting things did you learn today that you did not know before?

Further class and homework opportunities

Suggestions 1–6 on page 98 of this book

geog.1 workbook, page 33

geog.1 Kerboodle: see lesson presentation, worksheets, end-of-lesson assessment

Answers for 'Your turn'

1   a   A long-term reduction in the average temperature around Earth, leading to the spread of glaciers.

   b   A cold region where the ground is permanently deeply frozen. Only the surface thaws in summer, allowing small low plants such as shrubs, mosses, lichens, sedges, and grasses to grow. There are few or no trees, since their roots cannot penetrate the frozen ground. (Note: tundra is a biome, and the frozen ground is called permafrost.)

2   100 000 years; around 10 000 years ago

3   a   Water on land was locked into ice, so it no longer flowed back to the ocean. So water levels in the ocean fell. As a result, the more shallow parts of the ocean floor, between the British Isles and the rest of Europe, were exposed as land.

   b   Because as the ice age ended, and ice melted, water levels around the British Isles rose again.

   c   Answers will vary, but may include: our history would be different – we might be part of a different country now, and speak a different language; easier to reach other parts of Europe by road, making travel and trade easier; climate would be at least a bit different as we'd be part of a bigger land mass, with less coast; fewer seaside resorts; London might not exist, since no longer a port.

4   a   Some students may need help about where they are on the map.

   b   Answers will vary, but all students will need suitable clothing, food, and something to drink. Also a tent – unless they can sleep in the time machine? Sleeping bag? Source of solar power? Snow goggles? Helmet? Boots with a good grip? Skis or snow shoes? A weapon, just in case? Camera / video camera? Something to write on / with? Perhaps the time machine has equipment for sending messages into the future.

   c   You might want to give students a minimum word count. They could write about the cold, what the landscape looks like, the silence and emptiness, the absence of other people, animals they might see; they might write about their feelings – excitement, or fear, or loneliness.

Glaciers: what and where?

About this unit

This unit looks at what glaciers are, how they form, and how they flow. It also shows where they are found on Earth today.

Key points

- During the last ice age, about a third of Earth was covered in ice. Today, about a tenth is.
- The ice occurs as glaciers in Earth's coldest places.
- Glaciers form when layers of snow build up (over years) and compact to form ice, which eventually starts to flow. (Flowing is a key feature of glaciers.)
- Very large glaciers, covering big areas, are called ice sheets. They are found in Greenland and Antarctica.
- Glaciers on mountains slopes are called mountain glaciers (or alpine glaciers).
- Within a glacier, ice flows because the ice crystals slide over each other. The whole glacier also flows, when pressure causes the ice at its base to melt. It slides along on the water.
- Mountain glaciers flow down slopes. The ice in ice sheets flows out to where it is thinner.
- An ice sheet may flow into the ocean to form a floating ice shelf. Some of this breaks up, or calves, from time to time, giving icebergs.

Key vocabulary

glacier, ice sheet, mountain glacier, ice shelf, iceberg, crevasse

Skills practised in 'Your turn'

- Geography skills: q1, define; q3, interpret a map; q4, interpret a satellite image
- Literacy skills: q6, describe being stuck down a crevasse (if written answer)
- Thinking skills: q2, come up with reasons; q4, explain choice; q5 come up with ways to show that a glacier is flowing, and to measure its speed

Unit outcomes

By the end of this unit, most students should be able to:

- explain the terms given in 'Key vocabulary' above
- explain what a glacier is, and specifically, include the fact that a glacier flows
- explain the difference between an ice sheet and a mountain glacier
- say where glaciers are found on Earth today
- describe how glaciers form
- explain why glaciers are able to flow, and where they flow to

Suggestions for a starter

1. Show students an interesting / stunning unlabelled photo of a mountain (alpine) glacier. Ask them to make up questions about what it shows. (Prompt for What? Where? Why? How? questions.) Can anyone answer the questions?

2. Ask: What can you tell me about glaciers? Push for details. Write answers on the board. You can check back later. (Some students may have seen glaciers.)

3. Recap. Ask: When did the last ice age end? How long had it lasted? How much of the British Isles was covered by ice? How did it affect people in the British Isles?

4. Play an audio track of sounds from a glacier, from the internet, as a mystery. Ask: What do you think is making this sound? Then say you will ask again at the end of the class.

Suggestions for plenaries

Plan plenaries at strategic points throughout the lesson, as well as at the end.

Mid-lesson

1   After question 4, discuss photo A. Ask for comments on the shape. Who goes to Antarctica? Does anyone live there full time? Any animals? (Polar bars: no. Penguins: yes.)

2   Do 'Your turn' question 5 as a plenary.

3   Look at photo B. What do you think draws tourists to glaciers?

End-of-lesson

4   Write the following answers on the board. Ask what the questions would be. (Sensible ones, related to what you learned today!) Answers:

   a   a glacier   **b**   99%   **c**   an ice sheet

   d   they flow   **e**   a crevasse   **f**   sea ice

5   Write a set of say ten true / false statements based on this unit, on strips of paper. Sample statements:

   –   There are no glaciers in Africa.

   –   Glaciers are frozen rivers.

   –   Crevasses are where the ice has started to melt.

   Fold the strips and put them in a tin. The class plays Pass the parcel, with music. When the music stops, the holder chooses one, reads out the statement, and declares it true or false. Those who disagree put their hands up, and say why.

6   If you used starter 4, replay the audio now. Ask: What is making these sounds?

Further class and homework opportunities

Suggestions 7–15 on page 98 of this book

geog.1 workbook, page 34

geog.1 Kerboodle: lesson presentation, worksheets, end-of-lesson assessment

Answers for 'Your turn'

1   **a**   A large mass of ice, that flows across the land or down a slope, like a river of ice

   b   A very large glacier, that covers a huge area

2   Overall, the climate is too warm. And none of the mountains are high enough – and therefore cold enough – to have glaciers.

3   Students have a choice of over 40 countries. Answers might include some of these: Canada, the USA, Mexico, Chile, Argentina, Iceland, Greenland (Denmark), Norway, Sweden, Switzerland, France, Italy, Austria, Germany, Russia, Iran, Pakistan, Nepal, New Zealand, Tanzania.

4   Answer is **b**: over the South Pole – because it shows the complete land mass. Because Earth is round, none of Antarctica would be visible from over the North Pole. It is unlikely that any would be seen from above the UK. (It depends on the height of the satellite.) You could refer back to the globe and map in Unit 2.10.

5   **a**   Put a marker, like a flag, on the glacier and record its position relative to the valley side. Leave it for a period of time (months), then come back and see if it has moved down the valley.

   b   Measure how far the marker (flag) has moved. Divide the distance by the number of months, to find the speed per month, then multiply by 12 to get the speed per year.

   c   Put a set of markers (flags) across the glacier, at regular intervals. After a period of time (months) those in the middle will have moved further than those at the sides.

6   You might yell out in case the others have not noticed. You might want to describe the creaking sounds, and the ice closing in, and how you are feeling: panicky – or calm? You might try scrambling up the walls, but it won't be easy. Perhaps the others can pull you out. But they are not carrying rope, so might use clothing instead. Perhaps they fail, while the ice closes further, locking you in. Perhaps one has a satellite phone. Perhaps, just as the last chink of sky is disappearing above you, a well-equipped snowmobile arrives …

Glaciers at work

About this unit

This unit explains how mountain glaciers scrape and shape the landscape through erosion, transport, and deposition of material. It also explains the process of freeze-thaw weathering.

Key points

◆ A glacier shapes and changes the land it flows over.

◆ First it erodes or 'wears away' the land. Water under the glacier freezes around rocks and stones in the ground, then plucks them out; they in turn scrape the ground as they are dragged over it.

◆ Then the glacier carries away or transports the eroded material. Most is frozen into its base. Some is carried on top, where it fell from the valley sides. Anything that falls into crevasses is carried inside the glacier.

◆ As the glacier flows down the mountain, the front eventually reaches a warmer place, where it melts. So the transported material is deposited.

◆ This deposited material is a mix of rocks, stones, clay, and sand, called till.

◆ The meltwater from the glacier runs off, and will feed a river or lake.

◆ The result of erosion, transportation, and deposition is glacial landforms.

◆ Erosion is helped by freeze-thaw weathering, where water freezes in cracks in rock, expanding as it freezes. Over time, repeated cycles of freezing and thawing break rock into smaller pieces.

Key vocabulary

erode, transport, deposit, abrasion, plucks, freeze-thaw weathering, striations, glacial till, meltwater, snout, glacial landform, glaciated, glaciation

Skills practised in 'Your turn'

◆ Geography skills: q2, distinguish between processes and features; q2, q4, draw diagrams to illustrate geographical processes and features; q3–5, interpret photos

◆ Communication skills: q3, describe what's shown in a photo

◆ Literacy skills: q6, write a set of bullet points; q7, start a glossary

◆ Thinking skills: q1, q4–6, explain

Unit outcomes

By the end of this unit most students should be able to:

◆ explain the terms given in 'Key vocabulary' above

◆ describe the processes of glacial erosion, transport, and deposition

◆ explain how freeze-thaw weathering works, and how it affects glacial erosion

Suggestions for a starter

1 Play a time-lapse video clip from the internet, showing a glacier flowing. Ask for comments, in particular about how the glacier might affect the place it's flowing in.

2 Show an image of a glacier. Ask: Why do we bother studying glaciers in geography?

3 With books closed, show a photo of a glacier, and a photo of a big bulldozer. Ask: What's the link? Say that the question will be answered in this lesson.

Suggestions for plenaries

Plan plenaries at strategic points throughout the lesson, as well as at the end.

Mid-lesson

1 Before question 2, discuss the difference between *processes* and *features*. (Then you, or a student, could complete question 2 on the board, with help from the class.)

2 Use 'Your turn' question 5 as a plenary. Then ask students to say what else they can see in photo C. (A cave in the ice; glacial till; muddy sediment made of the fine particles carried by meltwater. Any sign of people?) What would happen if the temperature rose?

3 Draw a chunk of rock in cross-section on the board, with a V-shaped crack in its upper surface. Choose a student or students to add notes and further drawings to show how freeze-thaw weathering works. The class can direct, and suggest labels.

End-of-lesson

4 Write the word *GLACIERS* in big letters down the board, as the base for an acrostic. Ask students to fill in the horizontal words, using glacial terms they have met so far. Your letters can be in any position in their words. For example, S could start *striations* or be contained in *abrasion*. (Longer terms to try: *GLACIATION* or *GLACIAL TILL*.)

5 Hand out numbers on folded slips of paper, up to the number of students in the class. List terms from the lesson on the board: *abrasion*, *glaciation*, *striations*, and so on. Call out a number. The student chooses a term and gives a sentence about it. Call out another number. That student adds a bit more detail. Continue until each term has been explained in detail.

6 Ask: What did you find easy / difficult about today's lesson? Why?

Further class and homework opportunities

Suggestions 16–20 on page 98 of this book

geog.1 workbook, page 35

geog.1 Kerboodle: lesson presentation, worksheets, end-of-lesson assessment

Answers for 'Your turn'

1 It can pick up large amounts of solid material (including huge rocks), carry them away, and drop them somewhere else. Because it is so big, and heavy, and thick, it can scrape away a lot of material.

2 a You might want to discuss with students the meaning of *process* (in which something undergoes a change) and *feature* (a distinctive characteristic or part of something; it may be the result of a process).

Processes	Features
melting	meltwater
abrasion	striations
plucking	glacial till

3 It shows scratches and grooves in an area of flat rock. They are called striations, and are the result of abrasion by rocks and stones that were frozen into the base of a glacier.

4 Some was scraped from the sides of the valley by the glacier. Some may have fallen from above, as rock got broken up by freeze-thaw weathering.

5 a It is the water from melting ice. It looks milky because of all the tiny particles of rock in it. (These particles are called glacial flour, or rock flour.)

b It's here because the glacier has flowed down slopes to this place, where the temperature is high enough to make it melt.

6 a For example:
• Water freezes in cracks in rock.
• As it freezes it expands, making the cracks wider.
• Then the ice melts. The cracks fill up again with water.
• The water freezes, making the cracks even wider.
• After repeated freezing and thawing, the cracks get so big that the rock breaks up into smaller pieces.

b When the rock is in smaller pieces, it's easier for the glacier to pluck it out.

7 Remind students to include terms from Unit 4.2 too, in their glossary. They'll find definitions in the text, and in the glossary at the back of the students' book. As they work through the rest of the chapter, remind them to add further terms.

Landforms shaped by erosion – part 1

About this unit

This unit gives an overview of glacial landforms shaped by erosion, and then looks at three in more detail: corries, arêtes, and pyramidal peaks.

Key points

- Through erosion over thousands of years, glaciers create these landforms: corries, arêtes, pyramidal peaks, U-shaped valleys, hanging valleys.

- A corrie starts as a sheltered hollow where snow and ice build up, forming a glacier. This deepens the hollow by erosion, and eventually overflows it, moving down the mountain. When the glacier melts, the corrie is revealed. It may contain a lake (called a tarn in some places).

- Where corries form side by side, the glaciers erode the rock between them, leaving a sharp ridge called an arête.

- Where several corries form around a mountain top, the glaciers erode into the mountain top, forming a pyramidal peak.

- The overall effect of glaciation on a landscape is to leave it more rugged.

Key vocabulary

erosion, corrie, tarn, arête, pyramidal peak

Skills practised in 'Your turn'

- Geography skills: q1, interpret drawings; q2, q3, draw annotated sketches of places, from photos; and draw diagrams to show how landforms were formed
- Literacy skills: q3, write a blog
- Thinking skills: q1, decide whether a statement is true or false; replace false statements with true ones

Unit outcomes

By the end of this unit, most students should be able to:

- explain the terms given in 'Key vocabulary' above
- describe how glacial erosion changes a mountain landscape
- explain how corries, arêtes, and pyramidal peaks are formed
- identify these landforms in photos

Suggestions for a starter

1 With books closed, display stunning photos of corries, arêtes, and pyramidal peaks from around the world. Try for images with little or no snow. Say: These landforms have something in common. What do you think it is? Write guesses on the board. Then say the mystery will be solved during the lesson.

2 Recap. With books closed, write up a list of words from the last unit – *erosion*, *abrasion*, *striation*, and so on – but jumbled. Students unjumble each word and use it in a sentence.

Suggestions for plenaries

Plan plenaries at strategic points throughout the lesson, as well as at the end.

Mid-lesson

1   Ask a student or students to read out the text below the four drawings on page 68 of *geog.1* students' book. Then students compare the drawings, and call out how the landscape has changed over time. Say: The landscape in drawing 3 would have been under ice for thousands of years. Take a minute to try to imagine that.

2   Students read out the text below the drawings on page 68, about the formation of corries, arêtes, and pyramidal peaks.

3   *Arête* means fishbone in French. Ask: Why are these sharp ridges called arêtes?

4   Look at photo D. Ask: Why is a *pyramidal peak* called that? What would you expect to see at the other side of this mountain?

End-of-lesson

5   If you used starter 1: display the photos of landforms again, and ask what the link is. (All shaped by glacial erosion.) Ask students to identify each landform. (Note that corries have other names too: *cirques* from the French word for arena, and *cwms* in Wales.)

6   If you did not use starter 1: display images of corries, arêtes, and pyramidal peaks from around the world. Ask students to identify the landforms, describe them, and then say what they have in common.

7   With books closed, ask students to name and describe the landforms met in this unit. Ask: What do they have in common?

Further class and homework opportunities

Suggestions 21–23 on page 98 of this book

geog.1 workbook, page 36

geog.1 Kerboodle: lesson presentation, worksheets, end-of-lesson assessment

Answers for 'Your turn'

1   a   True

   b   False. A glacier deepens and widens a valley it flows down, leaving it U-shaped.

   c   False. A glacier creates sharp ridges and peaks, and deepens valleys. Overall, it makes the landscape more rugged.

2   Students should understand that the corrie itself is the landform, and the tarn sits in it. You could point out that the corrie in photo **A** looks like the seat of an armchair, and that the raised back wall of a corrie tends to be steepest part. For **b**, students could do drawings like those on page 69 of the students' book.

3   a   Students who choose photo **D** should be able to point out the two corries below the peak. The one on the right is more pronounced, from this angle. They are bounded by arêtes. The lake below the Matterhorn is called Riffelsee.

   b   Again, students could do drawings like those on page 69 of the students' book.

   c   Students might like to comment on the fresh air, silence, and peace. Walking on Striding Edge can also be dangerous, and climbing on the Matterhorn is very dangerous.

About this unit

This unit looks in more detail at two other landforms from the drawing on page 68 of the students' book, created by erosion: U-shaped valleys, and hanging valleys.

Key points

◆ U-shaped valleys and hanging valleys are created by glacial erosion.

◆ A mountain glacier flows down a river valley, widening and deepening it so that it becomes U-shaped.

◆ When the glacier melts, the U-shaped valley is revealed. It may contain a misfit (or underfit) river: a river clearly too small to have created the valley.

◆ Some U-shaped valleys contain long thin ribbon lakes. These show where a glacier flowed over soft rock, sandwiched between areas of hard rock. It eroded the soft rock more deeply, leaving a trough which later filled with water.

◆ A small glacier may flow down a slope to join a larger one. It erodes its valley less deeply than the large glacier does. So when the glaciers melt, the small valley is left hanging above the larger valley.

◆ If rivers flow in hanging valleys, they will drop as waterfalls.

Key vocabulary

U-shaped valley, misfit river, ribbon lake, hanging valley

Skills practised in 'Your turn'

◆ Geography skills: q1, interpret a photo, and draw an annotated sketch from it; q2, q4, draw diagrams to show how landforms are formed

◆ Literacy skills: q1, explain in a given number of words

◆ Thinking skills: q3, apply what has been learned, to a photo; q4, explain a name, and decide how to draw a diagram, where no example has been given in the text

Unit outcomes

By the end of this unit most students should be able to:

◆ explain the terms given in 'Key vocabulary' above

◆ describe how U-shaped valleys and hanging valleys are formed

◆ explain the link between hanging valleys and waterfalls

◆ explain what ribbon lakes are, and how they are formed

Suggestions for a starter

1 Recap. Ask: What glacial landforms have we come across already?

2 Recap. With books closed, write these on the board: *Bleaberry Tarn, Matterhorn, Striding Edge*. Ask what each is, and what it looks like, from memory. Some students may be able to sketch the landform on the board. Then say you are going on to two more landforms shaped by erosion.

3 With books closed, show a stunning photo of a U-shaped valley. (Not the one in the students' book.) Say: It was once a narrow valley. A glacier made it this shape. How do you think it did that?

Suggestions for plenaries

Plan plenaries at strategic points throughout the lesson, as well as at the end.

Mid-lesson

1   Ask a student to read out the text under the drawings on page 70 of the students' book.

2   Say: Compare the valleys in photos A and B. What differences do you notice?

3   Give students 3 minutes to study the sequence of drawings and text about hanging valleys. Then ask a student to explain to the class how hanging valleys are formed.

4   Do 'Your turn' question 4 as a plenary. Choose one student to do the drawings on the board. The class suggests the labels and notes.

End-of-lesson

5   Students look through the photos of glacial landforms on pages 68–71 of their books, then try to explain why glaciated areas attract tourists.

6   With books closed, list five glacial landforms created by erosion. (Note: waterfalls are not counted as glacial landforms; students will study them under *Rivers*.)

7   Give out modelling dough or similar to groups of students. They create models of the five glacial landforms covered in Units 4.4 and 4.5. Give prizes?

Further class and homework opportunities

Suggestions 24–27 on page 98 of this book

geog.1 workbook, page 37

geog.1 Kerboodle: lesson presentation, worksheets, end-of-lesson assessment

Answers for 'Your turn'

1   a   For example: A glacier flowed along here. It made the valley wider and deeper, through plucking and abrasion, and carried the material away. When the glacier melted, this U-shaped valley was revealed.

   b   Students should note that Keskadale Beck is much narrower than the road; it is more of a stream here, with many meanders. This long straight valley is a good place for a road, which runs near the bottom of the U.

2   Students can do drawings like those on page 71 of the students' book. They should not just copy the text, for their notes.

3   No, because a glacier would have filled this valley.

4   a   A long narrow lake in a glaciated valley; it is so called because it is long and thin.

5   Answers will vary. Encourage students to really try to imagine they are in that place.

Landforms created by deposition

About this unit

This unit is about deposition by glaciers, giving moraines, drumlins, and erratics.

Key points

- The material glaciers are carrying is deposited when they melt. The deposited material is called moraine.
- When the front of a glacier melts, a ridge of material is deposited at the front end. It is called terminal moraine.
- If the whole glacier melts, material is deposited along the sides as lateral moraine, and on the valley floor as ground moraine.
- Today the ground moraine may be gently rolling farmland.
- Large rocks carried by a glacier from elsewhere, and dropped where it melts, are known as erratics. They may be very different from the local type of rock.
- Drumlins are smooth elongated hills of glacial deposit. They are usually under 50 m high, and can be up to 2 km long. They are shaped like the back of a spoon. They show the last direction the glacier flowed in: from the more steeply sloping end of the hill to the shallower end.

Key vocabulary

moraine, till, terminal moraine, lateral moraine, ground moraine, erratic, drumlin

Skills practised in 'Your turn'

- Geography skills: q1, define; q2, use correct geographical terms; q3, q4, explain geographical processes
- Literacy skills: q6, unjumble words; q7, add to glossary
- Thinking skills: q3, explain and suggest; q5, deduce glacier's direction of flow from a photo

Unit outcomes

By the end of this unit most students should be able to:

- explain the terms given in 'Key vocabulary' above
- list the different types of moraine, and where they are found
- explain how erratics came to be in a place
- describe drumlins, and identify the direction in which the glacier flowed

Suggestions for a starter

1   Show a photo of a big impressive U-shaped valley. Ask students to remind you how it came to be like this. Then ask: So where did all the material that was carried away go?

2   Recap. Write up anagrams for erosion, transport, deposition. For example: *or noise, torn sprat, it poisoned*. With no advance clues, ask students to solve them. Then ask students to remind the class what each term means. Say they will look at deposition today.

3   Show a set of photos of moraines, drumlins, and erratics from around the world. Ask students to guess what they have in common. End up with the word *deposition*.

Suggestions for plenaries

Plan plenaries at strategic points throughout the lesson, as well as at the end.

Mid-lesson

1   Ask a student to read out the text below the drawings on page 72 of the students' book.

2   Turn to the photo on page 60 of the students' book. Ask: What signs of deposition do you see? And which drawing in Unit 4.6 does this photo match?

3   Ask: When a glacier melts, which type of moraine do you think there's most of? The answer is ground moraine, since it is deposited all along the glacier's length. The ground moraine from melted ice sheets is not usually more than 5 m thick – but can be up to 20 m thick.

4   Ask: Where is the ground moraine, in photo B? The answer is: everywhere, under the grass. See plenary 3 above. The clay and sand in it can produce good farmland.

End-of-lesson

This is a good place to pull together all the work in Units 4.3–4.6.

5   Traffic lights: give each student three squares of card, coloured red, amber, and green. Call out terms from Units 4.3–4.6. Students hold up green cards if they are confident that they understand a term, amber if they are not sure, and red if they do not understand it. Ask a green cardholder to explain it.

6   Start a spider map on the board with the main label *Glacial processes* in the middle, and sub-labels *erosion, transport, deposition*. Ask for words and phrases to build it up.

7   Write terms from Units 4.3–4.6 on slips of paper. Fold these and put them in a tin. Write the heading *Glaciers* on the board, and three subheadings: *erosion, transport, deposition*. A student comes up, takes a slip, and writes the term under the correct heading. Is it in the correct place? The rest of the class comments.

8   Call out the name of a glacial landform, or a process. Then start a stopwatch. A student speaks about the landform for 20 seconds, without repetition.

Further class and homework opportunities

Suggestions 28–35 on pages 98–99 of this book

geog.1 workbook, page 38

geog.1 Kerboodle: lesson presentation, worksheets, end-of-lesson assessment

Answers for 'Your turn'

1   a   The mix of rock, stones, sand, and clay carried by a glacier

   b   The material (till) deposited by a glacier

2   a   Lateral moraine

   b   Ground moraine

3   a   It is made of moraine, deposited at the snout of a melting glacier. As more and more till arrived, the moraine grew into a ridge. Over thousands of years, some of the rocks and stones broke down to soil, and vegetation grew. (You could discuss which way the glacier was flowing: right to left, or left to right. Remember, glaciers scrape out their beds.)

   b   Rocks and stones of different sizes, all mixed up

   c   A farmer could not use this strip of land for much. It's stony, and the ridge is in the way, should he want to use a tractor.

4   a   It was dropped by a melting glacier. (Because glaciers are solid, and thick, they can carry very large and heavy rocks.)

   b   Erratics are 'mistakes' in that they are usually a different type of rock from the rocks around them, and much larger.

5   The answer is **a**: from X to Y. Look at the main drumlin in the middle of the photo: the slope looks more shallow towards Y. (But it is not easy to tell from the drumlins in the background.)

6   They are the result of *deposition* by *glaciers*.

7   Check that students have included the new terms from previous units in their glossaries.

Glacial landforms on an OS map

About this unit

This unit explores an OS map, rich in glacial landforms, for part of the Lake District. Its scale is 1:50 000.

Key points

- 20 000 years ago, the Lake District was under an ice sheet. Today, it has many good examples of glacial landforms.
- Contour lines and labels on OS maps help you identify the glacial landforms.
- For a U-shaped valley, the contour lines are close together for the valley sides, and widely spaced for its floor.
- The U-shaped valley may contain a narrow 'misfit' river, or a ribbon lake.
- For a corrie, the contour lines are usually close together, and curved in a roughly horseshoe shape. They may enclose a small lake, which may be labelled *tarn*.

Key vocabulary

contour lines, grid reference, scale, U-shaped valley, corrie

Skills practised in 'Your turn'

- Geography skills: q1–8, interpret an OS map; q1, q3–6, match photos to grid references on the OS map; q4, work out the direction in which the photographer was facing
- Numeracy skills: q2, use the map scale
- Literacy skills: q2, complete a word; q7, use the glossary; q8, describe the area in the OS map using bullet points (or labels on a spider map)
- Thinking skills: q2, deduce what the blue contour lines in a lake tell you; q4, deduce what a beck is; q7, deduce whether crags are formed by erosion or deposition

Unit outcomes

By the end of this unit most students should be able to:

- explain the terms given in 'Key vocabulary' above
- identify U-shaped valleys, ribbon lakes, misfit rivers, corries, tarns, waterfalls, and crags on an OS map
- explain how they identified the above features
- match photos of glacial landforms to grid references on the OS map
- give four-figure grid references for specific features
- describe a glaciated area in some detail, using the information on the OS map

Suggestions for a starter

1. With books closed, ask: Who can remind me what OS maps are? What can I expect to see on an OS map? (You would expect answers to include contour lines.)
2. With books closed, say: Today we are going to look at a map of the Lake District. Who can tell me where the Lake District is? What is it like?
3. With books closed, display a photo of a mountainous part of the Lake District, perhaps with a lake, and preferably a low aerial shot. Ask students to describe the place. Then ask: How would you show the steep slopes, and the … on an OS map?

Suggestions for plenaries

Plan plenaries at strategic points throughout the lesson, as well as at the end.

Mid-lesson

1   Spend time exploring the OS map, to make sure students can interpret it. For example:
    –   There is a big forest on the map. Where?
    –   Give the names of three lakes shown on the map. Now name three rivers.
    –   Give a four-figure grid reference for: a square of flat land; a square of very steep land.
    –   Name a village shown on the map. Which square is it in?
    –   Find a farm on the map, and give me a grid reference.
    –   How would you get from Brackenthwaite to Buttermere by car?

2   After 'Your turn' question 1, ask: In which direction was the photographer facing? (Answer below.)

3   Repeat plenary 2 after 'Your turn' question 3. (Answer below.)

End-of-lesson

4   Discuss the answers to 'Your turn' question 8 as a plenary, to help students who have missed things.

    You could summarise as words and phrases on the board.

5   Ask: Did you find the work on this OS map easy / hard / interesting / enjoyable? Take a show of hands for each. Explore reasons for students' answers.

6   Ask: Which other parts of the UK might have OS maps like this one? (Answer: Scotland, Wales)

7   Ask: What kinds of people might find OS maps useful?

Further class and homework opportunities

Suggestions 36–40 on page 99 of this book

geog.1 workbook, page 39

geog.1 Kerboodle: lesson presentation, worksheets, end-of-lesson assessment

Answers for 'Your turn'

1   In square 1917. Now see if students can give a 6-figure grid reference, and say in which direction the photographer was facing. (Around 194175, and looking towards the north east.)

2   a   *ribbon* lakes
    b   Crummock Water; the blue lines show the depth of the lake, and it's at least 40 m in the deepest part.
    c   About 4.1 km, at its longest.

3   The answer is **c**: 1914. (The photographer was looking down towards the bulging end of the lake, from the slope in the right-hand side of the square.) Again you could ask in which direction the photographer was facing. (Towards the north west.)

4   a   A stream or small narrow river.
    b   It is flowing in a very wide valley: much wider than it could have shaped for itself.
    c   Look at Gatesgarthdale Beck (2014), Sail Beck (1817), and Mosedale Beck (1317): they all flow through wide valleys for at least part of their journeys. There are also some unnamed becks on the map, that look like misfits. But the rest appear to be in narrow valleys.

5   a   i   Bleaberry Tarn   ii   A corrie
    b   i   The photographer was looking down from a high point, over Bleaberry Tarn and Dodd to the curve on the right

bank of Crummock Water. (The left bank is partly hidden by Dodd.) He was in fact at the top of square 1614, on Chapel Crags.
        ii   He was facing north, and slightly east.

6   1517 (in the lower left corner)

7   a   There are many. Named crags in e.g. 1614, 1714, 1511, 2114, 2017, 1518, 1721, 1822; and unnamed crags in e.g. 1620.
    b   Erosion. They are in high exposed places, where rock is eroded by the action of freeze-thaw and other weathering. Softer rock around them was worn away, leaving the crags.

8   Students should recognise from the map – and related photos – that the area is mountainous and craggy, with steep slopes. There is a lot of water: three ribbon lakes and part of a fourth, several tarns, and dozens of streams and small rivers. There are several waterfalls too. As you'd expect, this rugged terrain is not crowded. There are two small villages on the low flat land – Buttermere and Loweswater – and several hamlets such as Brackenthwaite and Gatesgarth. There is one heavily forested area (the Ennerdale valley) and several other patches of forest. Note the number of National Trust symbols, indicating areas of scenic beauty. The car parks, hotels, and many footpaths also suggest that the area is popular with walkers / hikers. That means some people will earn a living from tourism. Some farms are also shown.

Glaciers and us

About this unit

This unit explores whether glaciers matter to us today.

Key points

◆ Whether they are still present, or long gone, glaciers have an impact on us.

◆ Glacial landforms create stunning scenery, which attracts tourists. For example, to areas like the Lake District.

◆ Glaciers around the world provide challenging environments for climbers.

◆ Meltwater from Himalayan glaciers helps to feed rivers which water farmers' crops, and provide a domestic water supply.

◆ Antarctica is claimed by several countries. Its ice may hide rich resources. The claims could cause conflict in the future. But for now, Antarctica is protected by a treaty.

◆ Ice sheets and glaciers are showing signs of melting, in response to climate change. Melting ice sheets will cause a rise in sea levels, which could be disastrous for many coastal communities.

Key vocabulary

tourists, meltwater, Antarctic Treaty, fossil fuel

Skills practised in 'Your turn'

◆ Geography skills: q5, interpret a photo

◆ Literacy skills: q5, fill in missing words

◆ Thinking skills: q1, q2, think of examples; q3, deduce consequences; q4, suggest reasons; q6, explain statements

Unit outcomes

By the end of this unit most students should be able to:

◆ explain the terms given in 'Key vocabulary' above

◆ give examples of opportunities that glaciers (past or present) provide for outdoor activities

◆ give examples of people who depend on glaciers for at least part of their water supply

◆ explain that some countries have already claimed part of Antarctica, and give at least one reason

◆ explain briefly what the Antarctic Treaty is

◆ describe how glaciers are responding to global warming, and what the consequences might be

Suggestions for a starter

1 With books closed, ask: Can you think of any ways in which the last ice age has helped people in the Lake District?

2 Ask: What if there were no glaciers? What difference would it make to the world?

3 With books closed, show one or more photos related to the content of this unit. For example, one of Scott's or Shackleton's expeditions, a scientific research centre in Antarctica, Everest base camp, a climber in Wales, a tour coach in the Lake District. Ask: what is the link between this / these, and glaciers?

Suggestions for plenaries

Plan plenaries at strategic points throughout the lesson, as well as at the end.

Mid-lesson

1   Several questions in this unit could be tackled with whole-class discussion.

2   For the photo in box 2 on page 76 of the students' book, say: The first two people to climb Everest took the Khumbu Icefall route. Their names were …? (Edmund Hillary, and Tenzing Norgay, a Sherpa.)

3   For the photo in box 4 on page 77 in the students' book, see if students can identify the flags. Note that the US has not made a claim on Antarctica, but has a research base there. The seven claimant countries are: UK, France, Norway, New Zealand, Australia, Argentina, Chile.

4   Box 5 on page 77 of the students' book is about Earth warming up. Say: This is usually referred to as *llbgoa graimwn*, or *eltmiac acnheg*. Ask students to unjumble the terms. (Global warming, climate change)

5   Look at the photos in this unit. Ask: Which place would you most like to visit? Why?

End-of-lesson

6   Ask: Who enjoyed learning about glaciers? Why?

7   Allow 3 minutes for students to write down the five most important things they learned about glaciers. Discuss their lists. Do all agree about what is important?

8   Write *GLACIERS AND US* down the board as the base for an acrostic. Students come up and write in words. Your letters can take any position in their words. (So C could lead to *PLUCKING*.)

Further class and homework opportunities

Suggestions 41–47 on page 99 of this book

geog.1 workbook, page 40

geog.1 Kerboodle: lesson presentation, worksheets, end-of-lesson assessment

Answers for 'Your turn'

1   Examples include: farmers who depend on the meltwater; farmers whose farms are underlain by glacial till; people involved in tourism in past and presently glaciated areas, including e.g. staff in hotels in the Lake District, and on tourist boats in Antarctica; guides and others supporting climbers on glaciers; scientists doing research on glaciers (linked to climate change), and glaciated landscapes; officials policing the Antarctic Treaty; manufacturers making clothing and equipment for climbers and researchers in glacial conditions.

2   Examples include: tourists enjoying the scenery in glaciated areas such as the Lake District, the Norwegian fjords (carved out by glaciers), the Alps, and Antarctica; hikers and climbers in glaciated areas, where steep slopes and icefalls may be a big challenge; people enjoy looking at glaciers in photos and films.

3   a   The Himalayan glaciers act as a store of water, building up when snow falls, and released gradually in the warmer drier months. If they disappeared due to climate change, water levels in the Indus (and other rivers) would be much lower in these months. So crops – and therefore children – would suffer. Also, in the wet season, rain would now fall in the Himalayas in place of snow. Instead of being stored and released gradually, the water would rush down the slopes and cause flooding. This would harm children too.

   b   There would be no glaciers on Everest, so the climb would be less of a challenge. (Climbers would also discover more bodies of climbers who had died and been frozen over.)

4   The land may be rich in metal ores and other resources, that lead to wealth. Ownership of a coast usually gives exclusive rights for fishing, oil exploration, and other activities off that coast. A base at the south of the world could be useful for strategic purposes (e.g., in time of war). People could go and live there.

5   a   It was much larger (the edge reached where the sign is).

   b   It is getting *warmer* in this region. So *less* snow falls. That means there is *less* snow to feed the *glacier*. So the glacier has *shrunk*.

6   a   Most scientists agree that we play a large part in global warming, by burning fossil fuels. (The carbon dioxide they produce is a warming gas.) Global warming in turn is causing ice sheets to melt.

   b   As ice sheets melt, water levels in the oceans will rise. So low-lying countries, and coastal communities, are at greater risk of flooding. Some low-lying places will disappear.

Most of these suggestions are addressed to your students. Where research or further resources are needed, the internet will almost certainly provide the answer.

The suggestions are graded *, **, *** according to level of difficulty. Some are suitable for all levels, and can be differentiated by outcome.

Your place ... 20000 years ago!

1   **Woolly mammoths**   They roamed the tundra in southern parts of the British Isles, during the last ice age. Find out more about these amazing creatures. How big were they? What did they eat? Why and when did they die out? Could do a wall display, a radio report, a web page, or printed pages for a children's comic.   */**

2   **Ice age animals**   Find out more about the animals who lived in, or migrated to, the British Isles during the ice age. Assemble a collection of photos.   */**

3   **It's tundra!**   The southern parts of the British Isles are no longer tundra. But there is still tundra on Earth today. Where? What is it like? What kinds of plants and animals live there? What about people? Write an article for a geography website.   */**/***

4   **The Little Ice Age**   Not so long ago Earth had a period of cooling called the Little Ice Age. In Britain, the River Thames froze over in winter. Find out more about the Little Ice Age and do a class presentation, or draw a strip cartoon, or write a magazine article.   */**

5   **Could there be another ice age?**   Well, could there? What might cause it? Find out, and tell us!   ***

6   **Hold on! You are living in an ice age!**   One-tenth of Earth is covered in ice. So, technically, we are still in an ice age! It began 2.6 million years ago. Find out more and explain to the class.   ***

Glaciers: what and where?

7   **Antarctica's ice sheet**   It is larger than the USA. It has 61% of all the fresh water on Earth. Find out more about the geography of this amazing continent. Write an article for a travel magazine.   */**

8   **Who discovered Antarctica?**   Find out. Tell us.

9   **Sir Robert Scott**   He died on Antarctica, in a race to the South Pole. Find out about his ill-fated expedition.   */**

10   **Iceland**   Is it made of ice? Is it covered in ice? Do some research about this exciting country.   */**

11   **Greenland**   Find a map of Greenland with its ice sheet marked on. Paste it onto card and add notes about Greenland around it.   *

12   **Ice caps**   Like ice sheets and mountain glaciers, they are another type of glacier. Find out more.   **/***

13   **Call my bluff**   Your team makes up pairs of statements about glaciers and ice ages, with one statement true and one false. Challenge another team. If the team gets it wrong, one point for you!   ***

14   **Adopt a glacier ...**   from anywhere in the world. Tell us about it.   */**

15   **Ötzi the Iceman**   Who was he? And where is he now?   */**

Glaciers at work

16   **Sketch a glacier**   Draw a sketch from the photo on page 67 of the students' book, and annotate it.   **

17   **Glacier gallery**   Make a collection of images of glaciers. You could stick them on card and annotate them.   *

18   **Freeze-thaw weathering**   You have to give an illustrated talk about freeze-thaw weathering to a climbing club. What will you say, and what will you show?   **/***

19   **Those icy words**   Make up three sentences of your own using the words *glacial*, *glaciated*, and *glaciation*.   *

20   **Anagrams**   One student chooses some key words from this unit and makes up anagrams, using an internet anagram engine. How quickly can the class solve them?   **

Landforms shaped by erosion – part 1

21   **Corrie**   See if you can find some photos of corries in Wales and Scotland. (In Wales they are called cwms.)   *

22   **Pyramidal peaks**   Several famous mountains have pyramidal peaks. See if you can name at least three.   *

23   **Missing words**   Type out a paragraph about arêtes ... or cirques ... or pyramidal peaks. Make it at least 25 words long. Then delete six or seven key words. Print it out and ask a partner to fill them in.   *

Landforms shaped by erosion – part 2

24   **My starring role**   Tell the story of a U-shaped valley, starting with a snowfall high on a mountain, as a strip cartoon.   **

25   **Valleys**   Find some pictures of U-shaped valleys and hanging valleys. Can you make a slide show? Don't forget to say where they are in the world.   *

26   **Get modelling!**   Make your own models of the glacial landforms created by erosion. Or one big model showing them all. (It could be like the fourth drawing on page 68.) What material will you use?   **

27   **Sketch the landscape**   Make a sketch from the fourth drawing on page 68. Label all the landforms created by erosion.   **

Landforms created by deposition

28   **More moraine**   See if you can find some pictures of moraine left by melting glaciers, or glaciers long gone. (Note: we use *moraine* to mean the material deposited on melting. In other places you may find it used in a more general way to mean the material being carried by the glacier.)   *

29   **Know your moraines**   Do a drawing that shows all three kinds of moraine.   **/***

30   **The lament of the lonely erratic**   You are an erratic – and a long way from home. Write a poem or a sad song.   **/***

31 Glacial bingo Each student is given a bingo card, with names of glacial landforms on, and other glacial terms (ice sheets, abrasion, till, etc.). The teacher then calls out something related to these. For example, it could be the definition of a term (*It is a mix of rocks and stones and sand and clay.*) or the name of an actual feature (*Striding Edge, the Matterhorn*). Who can tick them all off first? */**

32 Write an acrostic poem Choose a term related to glacial landforms – for example, *DEPOSITION* or *ERRATIC*, and use it as the base for an acrostic. But there's a snag. Instead of single words, make up lines of a poem. **/***

33 Glacial crossword Make up a crossword using terms about glaciers, glacial processes and landforms. Then swap with a partner – and fill each other's in. ***

34 Play Taboo Divide the class into paired teams to play this game – perhaps four or five in a team. There are two parts to the game. Each team follows the instructions below.

1 *First, choose the taboo words.*

– Choose six key words from those you have learned about glaciers, glacial processes, and landforms. Make a card for each.

– At the top write the key word, and in a different colour add five words that you'd want to use, if you were explaining the key word to someone else. (These become the taboo words.)

2 *Now play the game.*

– Swap all your cards with another team – but not your opposing team. (No team should have the cards it prepared.)

– Now, play the game with your opposing team. Each team takes turns. To play, a student chooses a card, hidden from the rest of his / her team, and then gives verbal clues, but without using any of the taboo words, to help the rest of the team guess the key word. They have just 1 minute to guess, but can make any number of guesses in that time.

– Meanwhile the opposing team must keep an eye on the clock and make sure that no taboo words are used. (So the opposing team must see the card that was chosen.)

3 *Then the teams reverse roles.* **

35 Glacial dominoes Give out cards with a diagram in one half, and an unrelated definition in the other. Students arrange themselves around the room so that a diagram matches the neighbouring student's definition. *

Glacial landforms on an OS map

36 How fast can you find it? A student (or teacher) calls out a feature or place on the OS map. Students have to find it and give a four-figure grid reference. This could be turned into a class game, against the clock, with a set search time for each item. Who found most? **

37 Model some more! A challenge. Choose an area from the OS map, and see if you could model it in modelling dough or similar. Complete with lakes? Blue thread for rivers? **

38 We'd like a field trip! Write a letter to your Head teacher suggesting that students should visit the Lake District on a field trip, and why. */**

39 Black Sail Hut A challenge: you have to find your way from your home to Black Sail Hut, a youth hostel in square 1912 of the OS map on page 75 of the students' book. Work it out! **/***

40 Come and visit the Lake District Design and write a leaflet to tell tourists why they should consider visiting the Lake District – tell them about the landscape, and what they could see and enjoy. **

Glaciers and us

41 The Antarctic Treaty Find out more and prepare a class presentation or write a short article about it. **

42 Antarctic debate 'This house declares that no country should be allowed to own Antarctica.' Which side are you on? Hold the debate. **

43 Global warming Earth is warming up. Prepare a short and dramatic report for TV about why experts think this is happening, and how it is affecting glaciers, and what the consequences of this might be. ***

44 Odd one out Students prepare sets of words for Odd one out, to try out on the rest of the class, using what they learned in this chapter. Perhaps three or four words in a set. **/***

45 Celebrate … glaciers Write a poem or song or rap about how great glaciers are. Or design a T-shirt. **/***

46 Glacier glossary Check that your glacier glossary ('Your turn' question 7 on page 67) is complete. Or if you didn't do one, do it now. *

47 Glacier snap Create pairs of cards, with a definition or drawing on one, and the corresponding term on the other. Then divide the pairs to form two sets, and play a game of Snap with a partner. (Or give each student one card. He / she has to find the person with the card that matches.) **

Rivers

About this chapter

Addressing the KS3 Programme of Study

- ◆ Understand how geographical processes interact to create distinctive human and physical landscapes that change over time
- ◆ Understand how human activity relies on effective functioning of natural systems
- ◆ Understand, through the use of detailed place-based exemplars, the key processes relating to hydrology
- ◆ Interpret a range of sources of geographical information, including maps and diagrams
- ◆ Interpret Ordnance Survey maps, including using grid references

About the content

- ◆ The River Thames is used as exemplar because it is the best-known river in the UK, it passes through our capital city, and it is steeped in history.
- ◆ The study of water resources is part of hydrology, so a unit on water supply is included. It shows how human activity relies on the effective functioning of natural systems.
- ◆ Floods are increasingly a feature of life in the UK, so the chapter has three units on flooding.

The big picture

These are the key ideas behind this chapter.

- ◆ A river is rainwater flowing to the sea; it completes the water cycle.
- ◆ We depend on the water cycle, and rivers, for survival.
- ◆ Rivers shape the land they flow over, by eroding, transporting, and depositing material. The result is the characteristic landforms and features found along the river.
- ◆ We use rivers in many different ways as they flow on their way to the sea. One major use is as a source of our water supply.
- ◆ Flooding in the UK is usually the result of heavy rain. It can cause a great deal of damage.
- ◆ We build flood defences to try to protect our homes, towns, and cities from floods.

A students' version of this big picture is given in the *geog.1* students' book opener for Chapter 5, and is the basis of the interactive self-assessment form on *geog.1 Kerboodle*.

The chapter outline

Use this, and their chapter opener, to give students a mental roadmap for the chapter.

- **5**   **Rivers** The chapter opener in the students' book is an important part of the chapter; see page 11 for notes about using chapter openers
- **5.1** **Meet the River Thames** Photos of the Thames from source to mouth, and a map
- **5.2** **It's the water cycle at work** How water circulates continually between the ocean, the atmosphere, and the land; and how the rainwater reaches a river
- **5.3** **A closer look at a river** The river's journey, and its long profile, channel, and river basin
- **5.4** **A river at work** How a river erodes, transports, and deposits material on its journey
- **5.5** **Five landforms created by the river** How V-shaped valleys, waterfalls, gorges, meanders, and oxbow lakes are formed
- **5.6** **Rivers and us** How we use rivers, with the Thames as example
- **5.7** **Our water supply** Where our water supply comes from, and waste water goes to; and the problem of drought
- **5.8** **Floods!** What floods are and the factors that contribute to them
- **5.9** **Flooding on the River Thames** The Thames floods regularly; this unit shows some photos, and explores one year's floods
- **5.10** **Protecting ourselves from floods** Different flood defences along the River Thames

Objectives and outcomes for this chapter

Objectives	Unit	Outcomes
Most students will understand:		**Most students will be able to:**
● what the water cycle is, and that rivers are part of it	5.2	● describe the water cycle and draw a simple diagram for it; say that we depend on it for survival, and why
● how rainfall reaches a river, during the water cycle	5.2	● explain how rainwater reaches a river, using the correct terms (surface runoff, infiltration, etc.)
● that rivers have different parts and features	5.3	● name, define, and identify the different parts and features of a river (source, river basin, tributary, etc.)
● that rivers shape the land by erosion, transport, and deposition of material	5.4	● describe the processes of erosion, transport, and deposition
● that these processes produce characteristic landforms and features along a river	5.5	● describe and identify a V-shaped valley, waterfall, gorge, meander, and oxbow lake, and explain how each was formed
● that we make a great deal of use of rivers	5.6	● give at least five ways in which we use rivers (with the Thames as exemplar)
● that we depend on rivers and aquifers for our water supply	5.7	● name rivers and aquifers as the source of our water supply; outline the steps in providing a water supply; say where waste water goes
● what floods are and what causes them	5.8	● explain what a flood is, and give heavy rain as the main cause
● that flood risk is increased by both natural factors and human actions	5.8, 5.9	● give at least three factors that contribute to flooding; explain the part each plays
● that we take steps to protect homes, towns, and cities from flood damage	5.10	● give examples of flood protection measures (four long-term, two short-term) and explain how each works
● that the River Thames is an important British river	5.1, 5.6, 5.7	● say where the Thames rises and which sea it flows into; name at least six settlements on it; give at least five other facts about it

These tie in with the outcomes for each unit, in this teacher's handbook, and with 'Your goals for this chapter', in *geog.1* students' book.

Opportunities for assessment

See the formal assessment materials for this chapter on *geog.1 Kerboodle: Lessons, Resources, and Assessments*. They include an extended assessment task, an exam-style question, end-of-lesson assessments, and a self-assessment form. See also the notes on pages 14–15 of this book.

Getting ready for this chapter

geog.1 Kerboodle contains plans and presentations for each unit, including interactive activities, animations, and worksheets.

About 'Your chapter starter'

The photo on page 78 of *geog.1* students' book was taken through a plane window, on an early morning flight. The Thames looks like a river of molten gold. You can see several of London's bridges, including Tower Bridge. Look for the line of small 'pegs' across the river – the Thames Barrier. A little below it, the morning sunshine catches the Millennium Dome. The meanders of the *EastEnders* logo show up clearly – but rotated. At the top of the photo is the Thames Estuary. Note what appear to be beaches, on parts of the river bank: the photo was taken at low tide. In which direction was the photographer facing? (East)

Meet the River Thames

help at a glance

About this unit

This unit looks at the River Thames – England's longest river – and its journey from source to sea.

Key points

- ◆ The River Thames begins as a small spring in the Cotswolds.
- ◆ From there it flows for 346 km to the North Sea, passing through London, and entering the North Sea at the Thames Estuary.
- ◆ Other rivers (tributaries) join it, so it carries more and more water as it flows along. It grows wider and deeper.
- ◆ A large section of the River Thames is tidal: from Teddington in south west London to the sea. (That is around 110 km, including the estuary.)

Key vocabulary

source, spring, river mouth, estuary, tributary, water level, tidal, high tide, low tide

Skills practised in 'Your turn'

- ◆ Geography skills: q2, draw and label a sketch map, from a map
- ◆ Literacy skills: q1, extract facts; q3, define
- ◆ Thinking skills: q4, explain facts; q5, decide, and give reasons

Unit outcomes

By the end of this unit most students should be able to:

- ◆ explain the terms given in 'Key vocabulary' above
- ◆ say where the River Thames rises and which sea it flows into
- ◆ name at least six settlements along the Thames
- ◆ explain what and where the Thames Estuary is
- ◆ say that part of the Thames is tidal, and explain why

Ideas for a starter

1 Ask students how many rivers they can name. As they call out, write the names of the board. Ask which are in the UK, and underline these. Then ask what all the rivers have in common (apart from water). Establish that they start on high ground and flow down hill. (There are also other shared characteristics).

2 Ask: What's our nearest river? Where does it start? Where does it get its water from?

3 Have images of Old Father Thames ready in advance. Explain that the Thames has been represented in human form in songs, stories, and statues. Ask: If you had to imagine the Thames as human, what would it look like? Then display the images you found. Do they match what the students imagined?

4 With books closed, display a picture of Thames Head, with some water on view. (It is often dry!) Say: Something very important starts here. What?

Ideas for plenaries

Plan plenaries for strategic points throughout the lesson, as well as at the end.

Mid-lesson

1 Look at the photos on page 80 of the students' book. Point out the stone pillar in the first one, marking the source of the river. Ask for observations about the photos. Ask: How is the river changing, from place to place?

2 Point out the bridges in the photos on page 80 of the students' book. Ask: Why are bridges so important to people? What would life be like without them?

3 Compare the photos of the Thames at high and low tide (pages 80 and 81 of the students' book). Ask: What differences do you notice? What does the word *tidal* mean? What do you think causes the tides? Encourage students to explain in as much detail as they can. Ask: What impact might tides have on how people use the Thames? Might they cause problems?

4 Ask questions about the map of the Thames on page 81 of the students' book. For example: Is the river straight, or winding? About how wide is the estuary, at its widest point? About what percentage of the river is tidal? (About 31%, including the estuary) Which seaside resort is marked on the map? Which of the other towns and cities have you heard of before? What do you know about them?

End-of-lesson

5 True or bluff? Divide students into two teams, and give everyone red and green voting cards. Each team has 2 minutes, working in pairs, to write one true and one false (but believable) fact from today's unit. Pair 1 from Team A read their statements as if both were true. Team B each hold up a card to show which statement they think is true: green for 1, red for 2. If the majority chooses right, team B scores one point. If the majority chooses wrong, team A get a point. Alternate between teams until everyone has played, or play against the clock. To save time, statements could be prepared in advance.

6 Give out maps showing a local river. Students identify the source, tributaries, settlements along the river, and so on. They could work out the length of the river. This could lead to a piece of writing describing the local river.

7 In 2011, UK comedian David Walliams raised over £1 million pounds for UK charity Sport Relief in a 10-day, 225 km sponsored swim along the River Thames from Lechlade to London. He said it was 'Really, really tough'. Imagine you are David Walliams, and write a short daily blog. Where are you? What can you see? How do you feel?

Further class and homework opportunities

Suggestions 1–3 on page 122 of this book
geog.1 workbook, page 42
geog.1 Kerboodle: see lesson presentation, worksheets, and end-of-lesson assessment

Answers to 'Your turn'

1 Any six facts from this unit; for location, students should be able to say that the River Thames is in the south of England, passes through London, and enters the North Sea at the Thames Estuary.

2 The sketch maps can be quite rough. They should show the tidal Thames stretching from the outer end of the estuary, all the way to Teddington.

3 It is the wide mouth of the river, where it enters the North Sea. Explain that it is a transition zone between the river and the sea. At its widest, it is 29 km across.

4 a On its journey, it collects water from all its tributaries.

b As the tide rises, salty sea water flows up the river and through London, mixing with the fresh river water. The resulting water is a bit salty (brackish).

c Water evaporates from the ocean around the UK and falls as rain. This reaches the Thames and its tributaries. So the river water pouring into the ocean is continually being replaced by rain. (The water cycle is covered in Unit 5.2.)

5 Students might not be aware that rivers provide two-thirds of the UK's water supply. But don't discuss this in too much detail here, since it is covered later in Unit 5.7.

It's the water cycle at work

help at a glance

About this unit

This unit explains what the water cycle is, how important it is, and how the rainwater reaches the river.

Key points

◆ Water cycles continually between the ocean, the atmosphere, and the land. This circulation is called the water cycle.

◆ Through the water cycle, salty water in the ocean is converted to fresh water on land.

◆ So we depend on the water cycle. We need fresh water to drink, and for our animals, and for crops.

◆ The water cycle has four stages:

   – evaporation of water from the ocean to the air, as water vapour

   – condensation of the water vapour to form clouds

   – precipitation (rain falling) from the clouds to the land

   – flow of rainwater over and through the land to rivers, and hence back to the ocean.

◆ Rainwater reaches a river by running over the ground (surface runoff), and seeping into it through the soil (throughflow). In addition, rain soaks down to form groundwater, which then feeds the river.

Key vocabulary

water cycle, water vapour, evaporation, condenses, precipitation, fresh water, surface runoff, infiltration, throughflow, groundwater, water table, impermeable

Skills practised in 'Your turn'

◆ Geography skills: q1, q3, draw and label diagrams to explain key processes

◆ Literacy skills: q2, find words to match definitions; q5, write a news report

◆ Thinking skills: q4, come up with explanations

Unit outcomes

By the end of this unit most students should be able to:

◆ explain the terms given in 'Key vocabulary' above

◆ describe the water cycle, and draw a diagram of it

◆ say why we depend on the water cycle for survival

◆ explain how rainwater reaches a river, in the water cycle

Ideas for a starter

1 Show images of a range of rivers from the Amazon to small local rivers. Ask: What do they all have in common? Where does the water come from? Where does it go?

2 Say: It rained today/yesterday… Ask: Where did the water come from? How did it get there? Where did it go? Build up the water cycle on the board.

3 Ask: Why is the sea salty? Why are rivers not salty?

4 From Kerboodle, and with books closed, display the drawing from page 82 of the students' book. Ask students to explain what it shows. Keep saying 'Tell me more' until they've told the whole story.

5 Ask: Do you recycle anything? What? How? Do you think it is a good idea to reuse things? Why? Explain: Earth's natural systems are very good at recycling! We'll see an example in this unit.

Ideas for plenaries

Plan plenaries for strategic points throughout the lesson, as well as at the end.

Mid-lesson

1   Ask: Why do rivers still flow when it is not raining? Where does the water come from?

2   Ask: What effect would an increase in evaporation from the ocean have on the other parts of the water cycle?

3   What if we … cover the ground with concrete?

4   If you did not use starter 3, ask students to explain exactly why rain isn't salty, even though seawater is.

5   Look at the photo on page 82 of the students' book. Ask: Who can explain the caption of this photo?

End-of-lesson

6   Ask: Could we stop the water cycle? (You could display the drawing on page 82 of the students' book.)

7   Ask: So … which stages of the water cycle help humans? How? (Note that Unit 5.6 is about how we use rivers.)

8   Explain: In Britain, in the past, many people got their water supply from wells. Where does the water in a well come from?

9   Encourage students to start their own glossary of terms about rivers.

Further class and homework opportunities

Suggestions 4–8 on page 122 of this book

geog.1 workbook, page 43

geog.1 Kerboodle: see lesson presentation, worksheets, and end-of-lesson assessment

Answers to 'Your turn'

1

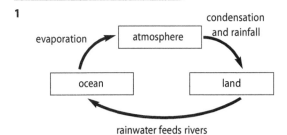

rainwater feeds rivers

2   The words are: A, groundwater; B, water vapour; C, infiltration; D, precipitation; E, evaporation; F, condensation; G, impermeable

3   The missing labels are: 1, surface runoff; 2, throughflow; 3, groundwater flow

4   a   It reaches impermeable rock at some point.

   b   Without rain, there is no surface runoff or throughflow to feed the river. The groundwater level will fall too, so there is less groundwater to feed it. And meanwhile, the river continues to flow to the sea.

   c   When it rains, groundwater levels, throughflow, and surface runoff all increase, feeding the river. But once the soil is saturated by heavy rain, runoff takes over – and it is fast, so the river fills up very quickly.

5   Students could say we are not coping very well: water levels in rivers are falling; water supply for homes and factories is now strictly limited; crops are beginning to fail and farm animals are suffering; there are food shortages already; supermarkets have long since sold out of bottled water and juice; there have been fights as people stockpile tinned foods, and fights over priority for water use; the army has been called in to take control, and so on. On the positive side, they could say that people are looking for affordable ways to convert seawater to drinking water.

A closer look at a river

About this unit

This unit takes a look at a river's course, from source to mouth. In 'Your turn', students apply what they have learned to the River Thames.

Key points

- The place where a river starts is called its source.
- From there, it flows downhill to the sea – or to a lake, or another river.
- The long profile of the river shows how its slope changes along its length.
- The area from which water drains into the river is called the river basin.
- The dividing line between one river basin and the next is called a watershed.
- Smaller rivers, called tributaries, join the main river. The point where a tributary joins the main river is called a confluence.
- A river can be divided into three parts – upper, middle, and lower course.
- The river carves out a channel, which changes shape along its course.

Key vocabulary

source, valley, tributary, watershed, confluence, river basin, floodplain, mouth, long profile, course, channel, cross-section, river bank, river bed

Skills practised in 'Your turn'

- Geography skills: q2, q5, interpret a map
- Literacy skills: q1, unjumble terms and define
- Numeracy skills: q5, arrange heights in decreasing order
- Thinking skills: q3, q6, explain

Unit outcomes

By the end of this unit most students should be able to:

- explain the terms given in 'Key vocabulary' above
- name, define, and identify the different parts and features listed above
- say that rivers flow downhill
- recognise that a river basin may cover a large area

Ideas for a starter

1 Show the movie *A river's journey*. It features the River Dart from source to mouth. Ask questions about the river and how it changes along its course.

2 In advance, write the lists below on the board. Refer students to the map of the British Isles on page 139 of the students' book (or display it). Ask them to work out where each river has its source and where it flows to. You could ask individuals to come to the board to join the correct answers with lines.

River	Rises in...	Flows to...
Spey	Pennines	English Channel
Thames	Grampians	Bristol Channel
Severn	Cotswolds	The Humber
Liffey	Exmoor	North Sea
Exe	Cambrians	Irish Sea
Trent	Wicklow Mountains	North Sea

3 Ask: Why do rivers usually start on higher land? And why do they grow as they flow to the sea?

Ideas for plenaries

Plan plenaries for strategic points throughout the lesson, as well as at the end.

Mid-lesson

1 Ask questions about the diagram on page 84 of the students' book. For example, which river basin do you think we're in? Are we on a floodplain?

2 Discuss the map on page 85 of the students' book. Note that the tributaries have tributaries! How do the experts decide where the edge of a river basin is?

3 After 'Your turn' question 5, say: The Thames rises 110 m above sea level. Imagine a height of 110 m. How many times higher than the school?

End-of-lesson

4 Write *source, valley, confluence, mouth, tributary, river basin, floodplain, estuary* on the board. Give students 4 minutes to study the drawing on page 84 of the students' book again. Then they close their books, draw a sketch map of an imaginary river with two tributaries, and label it using all the terms on the board. They swap drawings with a partner for checking.

5 Ask students to make up one question on any of the ideas or key words in this lesson. Nominate a student (X) for the hot seat. X then nominates three people in turn, to ask him / her a question. If X makes a mistake, another student takes the hot seat.

6 Write key terms from this unit on cards (one per card) and their definitions on separate cards. Hand one card out to each student. Students have to find the person with the complementary card.

Further class and homework opportunities

Suggestions 9–15 on page 122 of this book

geog.1 workbook, page 44

geog.1 Kerboodle: see lesson presentation, worksheets, and end-of-lesson assessment

Answers to 'Your turn'

1 The words are: A, course; B, mouth; C, valley: D, estuary; E, floodplain; F, watershed.

2 a Any three of the named tributaries.
  b River Cherwell
  c River Mole
  d i Abingdon   ii Reading

3 Luton is in the Thames river basin. Rain that falls there will find its way to the River Lee, and hence to the Thames.

4 No. Milton Keynes is not in the Thames drainage basin.

5 The places and heights, starting at the source, are: Thames Head, 110 m; Lechlade, 73 m, Oxford, 66 m; Reading, 45 m; Windsor, 29 m; Staines, 12 m; Thames Estuary, 0 m (sea level).

6 a A river collects water on its journey. The more water it carries, the wider and deeper it becomes. Its channel gets wider and deeper because the water wears away the land.
  b It enters the sea at its mouth. There, the river may be wide enough for ships to sail in (as with the Thames). So a settlement may spring up close to the river mouth, as a port. It will grow because of the trade. Also, fishing boats may deliver their catches there, which helps the settlement to grow.

A river at work

help at a glance

About this unit

This unit is about how a river changes the land it flows over, by eroding, transporting, and depositing material.

Key ideas

◆ Rivers change the land they flow over, through the processes of erosion, transport, and deposition.

◆ A river erodes (wears away) the land by means of abrasion, solution, and hydraulic action. Rocks and stones in it wear each other away by attrition.

◆ A river transports (carries away) its load of eroded material in solution, and as a suspension in the water, and as bedload, which moves along the river bed.

◆ When it reaches flatter land, the river deposits (drops) the material it is carrying, as sediment.

◆ The balance between erosion and deposition changes along the course of the river. Erosion is the main process in the upper course, and deposition takes over in the lower course, as the slope of the river flattens out.

Key vocabulary

erosion, erodes, solution, abrasion, hydraulic action, attrition, transport, load, suspension, bedload, deposition, deposit, sediment, V-shaped valley, floodplain

Skills practised in 'Your turn'

◆ Geography skills: q2, q3, interpret photos and deduce processes; q5, draw and label a diagram

◆ Literacy skills: q1, match terms to definitions

◆ Thinking skills: q4, choose, and explain

Unit outcomes

By the end of this unit most students should be able to:

◆ explain the terms given in 'Key vocabulary' above

◆ describe the processes of erosion, transfer, and deposition, using the correct terms

◆ describe how the shape of the river valley changes, as you move down the long profile

◆ say where erosion is the main process, and where deposition is the main process, along the river's course

Ideas for a starter

1   From Kerboodle, and with books closed, display the map of the River Thames from page 85 of the students' book. Say: Early this morning a fish in the North Sea swallowed a tiny fragment of Fred Smith's field. The field is over 200 km away, far up the river. How did this happen?

2   Show an image of a river. Ask: Do you think this river has always looked like this? Will it look like this in future? Do you think it's having any effect on the land it flows over?

3   Show some short film clips of different rivers around the world.

4   Display photos of waterfalls and gorges (to show erosion), sandbanks and estuaries (deposition), and muddy rivers (transport). For each photo, ask students to say how / where the river may be changing the landscape. Explain that there are different processes involved, which they will learn about in the next few lessons.

Ideas for plenaries

Plan plenaries for strategic points throughout the lesson, as well as at the end.

Mid-lesson

1   Ask a student (or students) to read aloud the text around the diagrams on page 86 of the students' book.

2   Say: Attrition helps a river to wear away its bank. True or false? (False. Attrition is where stones wear each other away.)

3   Give each student a card with one of the following terms on it; erosion, solution, abrasion, hydraulic action, attrition, transport, load, suspension, bedload, deposition, sediment. Call out 'upper course', 'middle course', or 'lower course'. Students hold up the cards they think apply to that river section.

End-of-lesson

4   Provide: a lump of rock, two smaller rough stones and two smooth pebbles, a small bowl of water, a plastic cup, and a sachet of coffee or sugar. Ask a pair of students to use them to demonstrate abrasion, attrition, and solution. Then ask students to think of a way to demonstrate hydraulic action (not necessarily in the classroom). For example, directing a hose onto a bank of earth?

5   Show photos or Google Earth views of: a) the Grand Canyon and Colorado River, b) the Yellow River in China (clearly showing a muddy yellow / orange colour), and c) the Nile Delta in Egypt. Ask: What river processes are going on here?

6   If you have done Chapter 4 already, ask: How do rivers compare with glaciers, in the work they do? Discuss similarities and differences.

Further class and homework opportunities

Suggestions 16–18 on page 122 of this book

geog.1 workbook, page 45

geog.1 Kerboodle: see lesson presentation, worksheets, and end-of-lesson assessment

Answers to 'Your turn'

1   Material is worn away – erosion

Material is carried away – transport

Material is dropped – deposition

2   **a**   Erosion. This appears to be a 'young' river in its upper course, where erosion is the main process. There are stones in its way and grass is coming right to its edges. It is eroding them. It is, of course, also transporting the material it erodes.

   b   **i**   The water wears away the river banks by continually pounding at them (hydraulic action). It dissolves any soluble material it encounters. It also picks up and carries small stones and other material, which then scratch against the banks and bed (abrasion).

      ii   While they are being carried, bounced, and rolled along, stones of all sizes scrape material from the bed and banks. Note that attrition is where the stones wear *each other* away.

3   **a**   Material eroded from somewhere else is being deposited here.

   b   It must be flowing slowly since it does not have enough energy to transport this material any further.

   c   No. Deposition like this does not occur in the upper course, where the river is flowing fast, with a lot of energy. (X is at a meander. Later, students will see that meanders are a feature of middle and lower courses.)

4   The water in the river in A is likely to be much cleaner since the river is not yet carrying a lot of material. The river in B looks as if it is carrying (and dropping) quite a lot of sediment.

5   This exercise helps to test whether students understand the various terms. Their drawings should be similar to the one at the top of page 87 of the students' book, but with much less text.

Five landforms created by the river

help at a glance

About this unit

This unit explains how rivers create V-shaped valleys, waterfalls, gorges, meanders, and oxbow lakes.

Key points

- ◆ Rivers create distinctive landforms, through erosion and deposition.
- ◆ V-shaped valleys form in the upper course, where a river erodes sharply downwards.
- ◆ Waterfalls develop where a river flows over a layer of hard rock, which has softer rock below. Waterfalls can retreat upstream to form gorges.
- ◆ Meanders are big loopy bends in a river, caused by erosion and deposition.
- ◆ Oxbow lakes develop when meanders are cut off from the main river.

Key vocabulary

V-shaped valley, waterfall, plunge pool, gorge, meander, oxbow lake

Skills practised in 'Your turn'

- ◆ Geography skills: q1, match landforms to processes; q2, q3, draw diagrams to show how landforms form; q5, interpret a photo, to deduce processes, and draw a sketch from it
- ◆ Literacy skills: q4, define
- ◆ Thinking skills: q5, make a prediction

Unit outcomes

By the end of this unit most students should be able to:

- ◆ explain the terms given in 'Key vocabulary' above
- ◆ describe and identify a V-shaped valley, waterfall, gorge, meander, and oxbow lake, and say how each is formed

Ideas for a starter

1   Ask students to recap the processes that go on in rivers (erosion, transport, deposition). Can they name any features that result from these processes?

2   Ask: What is the most exciting landscape you have seen? Ask some students to describe their choices.

3   Display images of river landforms. Challenge students to name the features. Ask for suggestions about how they were formed.

4   Show different samples of rock, named and labelled from hard to soft. Point out that they are all rocks found in Britain. Ask: Do you think they will all be eroded equally easily? Which might be the most resistant? Lead on to the idea that erosion may be slower in some places, faster in others. Explain that this will affect how a river shapes the landscape.

Ideas for plenaries

Plan plenaries for strategic points throughout the lesson, as well as at the end.

Mid-lesson

1   Ask: Is this unit about physical geography, human geography or environmental geography? Encourage students to justify their choice.

2   Ask: What's the landform in which Warkworth was built? (Refer to the photo on page 30 and the map on page 39 of the students' book.) Why was it built here? Could that have been a bad idea?

End-of-lesson

3   Provide a student with labelled samples of hard and soft rock (e.g. granite and shale). The student has to demonstrate how a waterfall forms.

4   With books shut, ask students to write the following statements, correcting them as necessary.

   a   Oxbow lakes are found in mountains.

   b   Waterfalls develop where there is soft rock above hard rock.

   c   Downward erosion in a river valley creates a U shape.

   d   The correct name for a bend in a river is 'loop'.

   e   Rain and magnetism carry stones and soil down the sides of river valleys.

   f   As waterfalls erode the rock, gorges advance towards the river's mouth.

   g   Deposition occurs on the outside of a meander, where water flows more quickly.

   h   One day, the oxbow lake will join up to the river again.

5   Ask: Why are rivers all different shapes? Why are they different lengths?

6   Write the names of the five landforms in this unit on separate cards: V-shaped valley, waterfall, gorge, meander, oxbow lake. Invite a student to the front of the classroom to describe, or act out, the term on the card, without using the actual word. The first student to guess correctly gets the next go.

7   Ask for names of sporting activities associated with rivers. (Fishing, swimming, rock climbing, canoeing, and so on) List them on the board. Which part of a river's course, or which river landforms, would suit each one best? (Alternatively, you could start by displaying images of these sports.)

Further class and homework opportunities

Suggestions 19–23 on page 122 of this book
geog.1 workbook, page 46
geog.1 Kerboodle: see lesson presentation, worksheets, and end-of-lesson assessment

Answers to 'Your turn'

1   V-shaped valley, waterfall, gorge: erosion. Oxbow lake: deposition. Meander: erosion + deposition.

2   Drawings could be based on the one at the top of page 88 in the students' book.

3   Students should start with the drawing in the students' book. Subsequent drawings could look something like this:

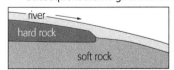 

4   **a**   A bend in a river

   b   It starts as a slight bend. As the water flows round the bend, it is forced to flow faster at the outer edge and more slowly at the inner edge. So the outer edge gets eroded faster and, eventually, material is deposited at the inner edge. So the bend becomes more and more pronounced. Diagrams should be similar to those at the top of page 89 of the students' book.

5   **a**   **i**   Erosion is taking place at A. The water flows fastest around the outer bend, wearing it away.

   ii   Deposition is taking place at B. The water flows more slowly around the inner bend, which means it has less energy, so it deposits material.

   b   One or both meanders could be cut off. The sketches could look like one of these.

   i   One meander cut off

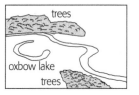

   ii   Both meanders cut off

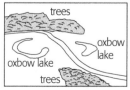

Rivers and us

About this unit

This unit looks at the ways we use rivers, with the River Thames as example.

Key points

- ◆ We use rivers in many different ways.
- ◆ The main use of the River Thames is as a source of water for our water supply.
- ◆ Water is also pumped from the Thames for use as a coolant in power stations, and in factories for washing and cooling things.
- ◆ Some is pumped out by farmers, to water crops, and as drinking water for herds.
- ◆ The river is used for transport of both cargo and people. (The Port of London lies towards the Thames Estuary.)
- ◆ It is also used for fishing, rowing, and other sporting and leisure activities.

Key vocabulary

settlement, water supply, power station, cargo

Skills practised in 'Your turn'

- ◆ Geography skills: q6, interpret an OS map and identify river uses
- ◆ Literacy skills: q1, summarise points as a spider diagram; q5, complete a word
- ◆ Thinking skills: q1, rank river uses in order of importance; q2–q4, make deductions about river use, and justify choices

Unit outcomes

By the end of this unit most students should be able to:

- ◆ explain the terms given in 'Key vocabulary' above
- ◆ list at least five ways in which we use rivers

Ideas for a starter

1 From Kerboodle, and with books closed, display the two lower photos on page 91 of the students' book. Ask: Have you ever used rivers for leisure activities? Tell us about it. What else do we use rivers for?

2 With books closed, ask: Do rivers matter to us? How? Why?

3 Challenge students to name as many rivers in the UK as they can.

Ideas for plenaries

Plan plenaries for strategic points throughout the lesson, as well as at the end.

Mid-lesson

1   Ask a student (or students) to read aloud the text under each photo on pages 90 and 91 of the students' book. Then discuss each photo. What part does the Thames play in each?

2   Ask: In which of the photos on pages 90 and 91 of the students' book is the Thames giving people a way to earn money?

3   Ask: In which of the photos on pages 90 and 91 of the students' book is the Thames making life easier, or more enjoyable, for people?

4   Use 'Your turn' question 1 as a plenary.

End-of-lesson

5   Hand out OS maps or tourist maps showing a local river. Ask: What clues does the map give about past and present uses of the river?

6   Ask: What if the River Thames dried up? As a class, create a mind map of consequences on the board. Encourage students to think about the environment, as well as the uses given in the students' book.

7   Challenge students to make up a conversation between two fish, about humans and their uses of the River Thames.

8   Challenge students to make up a blog, rap, poem, or soliloquy for Old Father Thames, about how humans use him. (He could reflect on how things used to be.)

9   Ask students to create a mind map: Why do people build near rivers? What are the advantages? Are there any disadvantages?

Further class and homework opportunities

Suggestions 24–28 on pages 122–123 of this book

geog.1 workbook, page 47

geog.1 Kerboodle: see lesson presentation, worksheets, and end-of-lesson assessment

Answers to 'Your turn'

1   a   Students should include all the uses shown in the unit.

   b   This could provoke some discussion. For example, is the river's role in the electricity supply more important than its use for transporting cargo?

2   Examples of uses of the Thames that are not likely to apply at Cricklade:

   • for domestic water supply (the river is too small at this point and water treatment plants are unlikely to be sited in a fairly remote rural area)

   • pumped out for factories (same reasons)

   • pumped out for power stations (same reasons)

   • for transporting cargo (the river is too shallow and narrow)

   • for rowing as a sport (same reasons)

   • for transporting people (same reasons), unless perhaps a couple of people in a canoe.

3   For spraying crops; crops are not grown in central London. (People do fish there.)

4   Leisure activities such as fishing, walking by the river, picnics on the river bank. People are drawn to rivers, whether in rural areas or in towns and cities.

5   Hydroelectricity

6   The towing path (6577) dates from the days when barges carrying cargo had to be towed along, in places, from the river bank. The water mill (6676) dates from when running water was used to drive machinery. The lock (6676) is a sign that the river was once used to transport cargo – and is now used by leisure craft; the marina (6675) is another sign of boating for leisure. The green markings along the river are footpaths.

Our water supply

About this unit

This unit describes how we use rainwater as our water supply, via rivers and aquifers.

Key ideas

◆ In the UK, about two-thirds of our water supply is pumped from rivers, and one-third from aquifers.

◆ Aquifers are underground structures of porous rock that hold a large quantity of groundwater.

◆ The water is cleaned up as required at water treatment plants, and stored in covered reservoirs until it's needed. Then it is pumped in underground pipes to our homes.

◆ Waste water goes down the drain to the sewage works. There it is cleaned up and put back in the river.

◆ Water supply in the Thames basin is a challenge, because the area has a very large population – but does not get that much rain. So drought, and hosepipe bans, are quite common.

◆ A desalination plant beside the tidal Thames converts salty Thames water into clean drinkable water. It can provide water for 1 million people a day.

Key vocabulary

water treatment plant, storage reservoir, aquifer, sewage pipe, sewage treatment plant, abstracting, drought, desalination plant

Skills practised in 'Your turn'

◆ Geography skills: q2, draw a flowchart to summarise the steps in which rainwater is converted to tap water

◆ Literacy skills: q1, define; q4, write a list

◆ Thinking skills: q3, q5, decide, and justify the decision; q4, come up with suggestions

Unit outcomes

By the end of this unit most students should be able to:

◆ explain the terms given in 'Key vocabulary' above

◆ say that here in the UK we obtain our water supply from both rivers and aquifers

◆ outline the steps in providing a water supply

◆ say what happens to waste water when we have finished with it

Ideas for a starter

1 Hold up a glass of clean water. Ask: Where did this come from? If students say 'A tap', ask: Where before the tap? and so on, until you arrive at 'A river'. So why does it look so clean? Why is it safe to drink?

2 Ask students to make a list of things at home that use water. Ask: Which ones need water that is clean enough to drink, and which ones don't?

3 What happens to all the waste water from your house? Where does it go? (To the sewage works, then back to the river)

4 Say: One summer, Megan's village had a hosepipe ban. Invite students to explain what a hosepipe ban is, and what it has to do with the weather and the water supply.

Ideas for plenaries

Plan plenaries for strategic points throughout the lesson, as well as at the end.

Mid-lesson

1   Ask students to read aloud the text for each stage of the diagram on page 92 of the students' book. Discuss each stage. Ask: Are there any reservoirs or water treatment plants in your area?

2   Challenge students to find the sewage works for Amble, on the OS map on page 39 of the students' book. Ask: Why was this spot was chosen for the works?

3   Turn back to the rainfall map on page 51 of the students' book. Ask: What can you say about the rainfall in the Thames basin area?

4   Ask: Do you leave the tap running while you clean your teeth? You could be wasting up to 9 litres of water a minute! In 1830, people in the UK used an average of 18 litres of water a day per person. We now use about 150 litres. Why do we use so much more now than then?

End-of-lesson

5   Ask students to look back at the photo on page 82 of the students' book. Then write the caption on the board: Borrowing from the water cycle. All students stand up. In turn, each makes a statement about the processes and steps by which we borrow water from the water cycle, and then return it. The speaker then sits down. (You can decide whether to reject repeat statements, or have the class point out repeats.)

6   Ask: What are the main pressures on water supply? You could give hints: weather, climate change, growing population, greater per capita use.

7   Ask: What would be the biggest inconvenience to you if the water supply to your house were cut off?

Further class and homework opportunities

Suggestions 29–34 on page 123 of this book

geog.1 workbook, page 48

geog.1 Kerboodle: see lesson presentation, worksheets, and end-of-lesson assessment

Answers to 'Your turn'

1   a   Groundwater is water that has soaked through the ground and filled up cracks in the rock below. Aquifers are layers of rock that hold a large amount of groundwater.

   b   The rest comes from rivers.

2   Students can choose to show a water supply from aquifers or from rivers. Or they could draw a branching flowchart that covers both options. Below are sample stages:

Water supply from a river

1)   Rain falls.
2)   It reaches the river by running over the ground and soaking through it.
3)   Water is pumped from the river into a reservoir.
4)   From the reservoir, it goes to a water treatment plant to be cleaned up.
5)   Then it goes to a storage reservoir.
6)   From the reservoir, it is pumped to my house.
7)   It flows out when I turn the tap on.
8)   I wash my hands and the waste water goes down the plug hole.
9)   It goes to a sewage works to be cleaned up.
10) From the sewage works, it goes back into the river.

Water supply from an aquifer

1)   Rain falls.
2)   It soaks through the ground into an aquifer.
3)   Water is pumped from the aquifer to a water treatment plant to be cleaned up.
4)   Then it goes to a storage reservoir.
5)   From the reservoir it is pumped to my house, etc.

3   There are reservoirs and plants to build, pumps and chemicals to buy, and underground pipes to lay to every house, and to repair when they leak. There will be a big electricity bill for the pumps, lots of staff to pay, and vehicles to run.

4   Students might suggest things like: take a quick shower rather than a bath; don't always flush the loo (or put a brick in the cistern); use waste water on garden plants; turn off the tap when brushing teeth; use 'quick wash' settings for washing machines and dishwashers, etc.

5   It is a good idea in theory, given the endless supply of seawater. But point out that it is uses a lot of electricity. It works well for countries that are rich in fossil fuels (and therefore have cheap electricity) or that are well placed for solar power.

Floods!

About this unit

This unit explains what floods are, and explores factors that increase the flood risk.

Key points

◆ Floods occur when a river receives more water than its channel can hold. So the water overflows the banks.

◆ Floods are usually the result of heavy rain.

◆ Flash floods are sudden floods caused by a burst of very heavy rain.

◆ Flooding is natural, and occurs on the floodplain. So if we live on a floodplain, we can expect floods!

◆ Anything that restricts infiltration will increase the flood risk, by increasing surface runoff.

◆ These natural factors increase the flood risk:
  – impermeable rock in the river basin (rain can't soak through)
  – saturated soil (won't take more water)
  – steep slopes (promote runoff)
  – many tributaries (so the river receives water from a large basin).

◆ We humans also increase the flood risk by:
  – cutting down trees (which promote infiltration)
  – concreting over the soil (reducing the area available for infiltration)
  – connecting street drains to the river (via the sewage system).

Key vocabulary

flood, floodplain, infiltration, surface runoff, flash flood, impermeable rock, tributary

Skills practised in 'Your turn'

◆ Geography skills: q1, q2, interpret drawings

◆ Literacy skills: q2, write a list to summarise

◆ Thinking skills: q1, arrange in logical order; q2, classify and deduce; q3, deduce and think of solutions

Unit outcomes

By the end of this unit most students should be able to:

◆ explain the terms given in 'Key vocabulary' above

◆ say what floods are, and give heavy rain as the main cause

◆ give at least three factors that contribute to flooding, and explain the part each plays

Ideas for a starter

1 Outside, get students to demonstrate the different rates of infiltration on different surfaces such as grass, gravel, soil, rock, tarmac, and on a steep slope. Help them to make the connection between infiltration and flooding.

2 Ask: What do you think causes floods? Where do you think is more likely to get flooded – near the mouth of a river or near its source? Why do you think so?

3 Ask: Who has seen stories about flooding in the news? Who has been affected by flooding? Tell us about it.

Ideas for plenaries

Plan plenaries for strategic points throughout the lesson, as well as at the end.

Mid-lesson

1 Ask students to read out the text for each of the diagrams on pages 94 and 95 of the students' book.

2 Use 'Your turn' question 1 as a plenary.

3 After doing 'Your turn' question 3, refer to the photo of Warkworth on page 30 of the students' book. Ask: Do you think Warkworth is in a flood plain? Make sure students give evidence. Now turn to the OS map of Warkworth on page 39. Ask: Do you still think the same?

4 Use 'Your turn' question 2 as a plenary. You could invite students to add to a spider map on the whiteboard.

5 Ask: What is a flash flood? How is it different from other floods? What makes it so dangerous?

End-of-lesson

6 Ask students to present their suggestions for 'Your turn' question 3b to the class. They could take a vote on the best one.

7 Ask: If no one lived on flood plains, would there still be floods?

8 Ask: Which part of a river is most likely to flood – the upper, middle, or lower course? Why?

9 Say: You are thinking of buying a house in a town that is located along a river. What information would you want to know about the river and the location of the house? Who could you ask?

Further class and homework opportunities

Suggestions 35 and 36 on page 123 of this book

geog.1 workbook, page 49

geog.1 Kerboodle: see lesson presentation, worksheets, and end-of-lesson assessment

Answers to 'Your turn'

1 Correct order: Heavy rain falls for a long period. The ground gets soaked. Infiltration slows down. More rain runs over the ground and into the river. The river fills up with water. The water rises over the banks.

2 **a** Students should use the factors given on page 95 of the students' book.

b They should underline them as indicated in this table.

Natural factors	Human factors
heavy rain	loss of trees
very wet soil	soil built over

Natural factors	Human factors
impermeable rock	blocked drains
steep slopes	street drains leading to river
tributaries	

c Human factors

3 **a** **i** Nobody lives at X   **ii** Lots of people live around Y

b Students might suggest building a high wall along the river. Ask what the advantages and disadvantages of this would be. For example, what about the view? (There is more about flood defences in Unit 5.10.)

Flooding on the River Thames

help at a glance

About this unit

This unit shows photos of flooding in different places along the River Thames, in different years. In 'Your turn', the reasons for the floods in 2012 are explored in some detail.

Key ideas

◆ Almost every year, there is flooding somewhere along the River Thames.

◆ Prolonged heavy rainfall is the main reason.

◆ People living on the floodplain, close to the river, are likely to suffer.

◆ An OS map will give clues about areas likely to flood.

Key vocabulary

saturated (in 'Your turn')

Skills practised in 'Your turn'

◆ Geography skills: q5, q6, interpret an OS map; q7, interpret photos

◆ Numeracy skills: q1–q4, interpret a bar chart showing monthly rainfall

◆ Literacy skills: q7, write a newspaper report

◆ Thinking skills: q2–q5, explain, give reasons; q6, come up with suggestions; q7, deduce damage, from photos

Unit outcomes

By the end of this unit most students should be able to:

◆ explain the term given in 'Key vocabulary' above

◆ say that there is flooding somewhere along the River Thames almost every year

◆ interpret a bar chart showing monthly rainfall

◆ identify a floodplain on an OS map

Ideas for a starter

1 Use the Environment Agency website to show the flood risk assessment for Twickenham, Marlow, Abingdon, and/or Oxford. Select *Check if you are at risk from flooding* on the home page and then type the place name in the Flood map box. Ask students to suggest reasons for the high-risk zones.

2 With books closed, say: Rivers often flood. It is completely natural! So why is it a problem for us? Who created the problem?

Ideas for plenaries

Plan plenaries for strategic points throughout the lesson, as well as at the end.

Mid-lesson

1   Look at the photos on page 96 of the students' book in turn. For each, ask: What kind of place is shown here? Who or what would have been disrupted by this flooding?

2   Before 'Your turn' question 1, make sure students can interpret the bar graph for rainfall. Ask: What do those red bars mean? What does *the long term average* mean? Was the rainfall for March above average, or below?

3   Before 'Your turn' question 5, make sure students can interpret the OS map. What colour is the river? What are all those little boxes? What are those orange lines called? What do they show?

End-of-lesson

4   Use the Environment Agency website (see starter 1) to check out the flood risk for the school area and other local places. Compare with one of the maps used in starter 1.

5   As a class, look at Purley on Google Earth. Does the image give any clues about the flood risk? Which offers more clues, the OS map or the Google Earth image?

6   Show photos of the extensive flooding along the Thames in 2013. Discuss each one.

7   Say: The Environment Agency is responsible for predicting floods, and warning people. Why is predicting floods so important?

8   Debate: We need new houses for our growing population. Should we build them on flood plains? (There are no easy answers!)

Further class and homework opportunities

Suggestions 37–40 on page 123 of this book

geog.1 workbook, page 50

geog.1 Kerboodle: see lesson presentation, worksheets, and end-of-lesson assessment

Answers to 'Your turn'

1   **a**   About 65 mm
    b   Drier

2   Because of the dry winter, groundwater levels were low. That meant less groundwater to feed the river – so the river level fell – and less in aquifers. As water continued to be pumped out for the water supply, the levels would fall further. So, in order to reduce the demand for water, people were forbidden to use hosepipes.

3   Because the soil was dry, it could soak up a lot of water.

4   **a**   There was above-average rainfall in four of the months from April to October inclusive. In fact there was over twice the average in April and June. So by the end of October, the ground could not soak up any more.
    b   In November and December, rainfall was well above average. Because the ground was already saturated, the rain could not soak away. Instead it ran directly to the river, causing floods in both months.

5   **a**   There are few or no contour lines between Purley and the river; for example, look in square 6676, which suggests flat or almost flat land – a floodplain.
    b   The land in 655762 is more elevated and a lot further from the river. So a house in 668764 is more likely to flood.

6   Students might suggest high banks or a wall – or even changing the course of the river. Ask about the advantages and disadvantages of any proposed solution. For example, what about the river view? What about the cost? (You could come back to this after Unit 5.10.)

7   Encourage students to use what they already know about home furnishing and fittings (sofas, flooring, low power points, etc.) and supermarkets (low bottom shelves) to help them imagine the damage.

Protecting ourselves from floods

help at a glance

About this unit

This unit is about ways to reduce the risk of flooding, and protect ourselves from floods.

Key points

◆ Flooding kills, and ruins homes and businesses.

◆ Flood damage costs a fortune to repair.

◆ There are ways to protect ourselves against flooding. Some are intended to be long-term solutions. Some are temporary, implemented when floods are on the way.

◆ The Environment Agency is responsible for deciding about flood protection measures for the public. (Individuals can also take steps to protect their own homes.)

◆ The Thames Barrier protects London from flooding by the sea.

Key vocabulary

long-term solution, short-term solution, embankment, local council, portable flood barrier, anti-flood shutters, sandbags, Thames Barrier, Environment Agency

Skills practised in 'Your turn'

◆ Geography skills: q1, interpret photos; q2, q3, q6, draw sketch map and diagrams, sketch design

◆ Literacy skills: q4, define; q5, write a response to an opinion

◆ Thinking skills: q1, q2, assess solutions; q2, explain; q5, evaluate opinion, and decide on a response; q6, come up with ideas for a flood-proof house

Unit outcomes

By the end of this unit most students should be able to:

◆ explain the terms given in 'Key vocabulary' above

◆ explain the difference between long-term and short-term solutions

◆ give four examples of long-term solutions for flood protection, and say how they work

◆ give two examples of short-term solutions for flood protection, and say how they work

Ideas for a starter

1   Group students into threes or fours (with books closed). Give each group a marker pen and sugar paper. Ask students to think of ways to prevent flooding. The groups share their ideas with the whole class.

2   Explain: In times of high flood risk, the Environment Agency issues warnings to inform people of the risks in their area. Three levels of warning are updated every 15 minutes. Ask students to design a symbol for each of the following warning levels:

–   Flood Alert: Flooding is possible. Be prepared.

–   Flood Warning: Flooding is expected. Immediate action required.

–   Severe Flood Warning: Severe flooding. Danger to life.

3   Play a news clip of flooding, showing the impact on people's lives and damage to their property.

4   Say: Imagine your house is flooded by dirty water from a river. Carpets, furniture, fridge – everything is ruined, and smells foul. Some of your things can never be replaced. How would you feel? This is the reality for thousands of people in the UK each year – and it is becoming more common.

Ideas for plenaries

Plan plenaries for strategic points throughout the lesson, as well as at the end.

Mid-lesson

1   Ask students to read aloud the text under the photos of flood defences on pages 98 and 99 of the students' book.

2   Spend time on each photo on pages 98–99 of the students' book, including the one of the Thames Barrier.
What do students notice? How does each solution work?

3   What problems might the building of embankments along rivers cause?

4   What can people do to help themselves if floods are predicted?

5   Ask: What methods could the Environment Agency use, to warn people of floods?

End-of-lesson

6   Divide students into small groups. Each group takes one approach to flood control and thinks out its advantages and disadvantages. Feedback is given to the whole class.

7   Debate: How long term is a long-term solution? What if global warming brings ever more serious floods? Can we ever truly protect ourselves from flooding? Should we just give up and move?

8   When built, the Thames Barrier was the most expensive civil engineering project in the world. Ask: Why was it thought to be worth spending so much money on it? They may need to build a new one soon!

9   Ask students to imagine that floodwater is heading for their homes. Ask: What can you do to protect your house, yourself, and your possessions? Which is the most important of the three?

10   Give students sugar paper and coloured markers to produce a mind map about all they have learned about rivers (in general, not just the Thames).

Further class and homework opportunities

Suggestions 41–48 on page 123 of this book

geog.1 workbook, page 51

geog.1 Kerboodle: see lesson presentation, worksheets, and end-of-lesson assessment

Answers to 'Your turn'

1   **a** A, B   **b** C   **c** D   **d** A, B

2   Answers will vary, but C and D should figure somewhere.

3   **a** Embankments are raised banks. If they are high enough, they will keep the river in when it swells with floodwater.

b A new channel carries water away from a river, reducing the water level. So there is less chance of the river overflowing its banks during floods.

c Fields can hold a large volume of floodwater. So there is less floodwater to reach homes. The floodwater will slowly soak away through the soil, without doing damage.

4   Because they are implemented only when there are warnings of floods on the way and only for the duration of the floods.

5   A good idea in theory, but it would cost a fortune. And where would they all go? Where there are lots of homes and businesses at risk of flooding, the usual answer is to put flood defences in place. (But if climate change brings us more rain, and worse flooding, it may be difficult to keep enough building defences to cope.)

6   Students could think about stilt houses or amphibious houses that float on the water as it rises. Doors and windows could have anti-flood shutters. Within the house, they could think of tiled flooring throughout the ground floor, raised power points, shelves sitting well above the floor, and so on. They should also think about furniture and appliances.

Further suggestions for class and homework

Most of these suggestions are addressed to your students. Where research or further resources are needed, the internet will almost certainly provide the answer.

The suggestions are graded *, **, *** according to level of difficulty. Some are suitable for all levels, and can be differentiated by outcome.

Meet the River Thames

1   **The Cotswolds** The nursery of the infant Thames. Find out more about the Cotswolds, and present the information in any form you choose. Add a map. */**/***

2   **Tidal Thames** What causes tides? Find out, and then prepare a presentation for a class of nine-year-olds! You can add diagrams if that helps. ***

3   **Track the Thames on Google Earth** Look it up. See how much of it you can track. Have a good look at the Thames Estuary. */**/***

It's the water cycle at work

4   **The illustrated water cycle** Draw a circular flow chart to show the water cycle. Do drawings (e.g. of clouds and a river) to illustrate the different parts. Or cut out suitable photos from magazines and stick them around your chart. *

5   **The precipitation poster** Precipitation can take several forms. Make a poster, using pictures cut from papers or magazines, to illustrate the forms it can take. *

6   **Cool clouds!** Clouds are an important part of the water cycle, and they come in different styles. Find out about the different kinds of clouds and write a report. Illustrate it with a photo or drawing of each type of cloud. **

7   **Cloud diary** Using a digital camera, take pictures of the same piece of sky every day, for the rest of this project. Label the different kinds of clouds. **

8   **Cloud poem** Imagine you are a river. Write a poem about clouds, from the river's point of view! */**/***

A closer look at a river

9   **Cities and their rivers in the British Isles** Using an atlas, find 12 cities in the British Isles that are on rivers. Mark the rivers and cities on an outline map of the British Isles. *

10   **Capital cities and their rivers** Find 12 capital cities in the world that are on rivers (not more than 5 in Europe). Mark the cities and rivers on an outline map of the world. *

11   **Adopt a river** Choose any river in the UK, except the Thames. (It could be a small local river, or a big one.) Draw a sketch map to show where it is, and which counties and towns it runs through. Now find out everything you can about it. */**/***

12   **Adopt an overseas river** Choose a river on another continent and find out all you can about it. Write a report for the class. (Tell students you want rivers from every continent, or for every letter of the alphabet.) */**/***

13   **Guess this river!** Choose a river from inside or outside the British Isles. Write down three facts about it – but keep its name secret. For example, you could name the country, the high land where the river rises, and a town or city on it. The class uses an atlas to identify the river. (This could become a class game, with a scoring system.) **

14   **River story** Find a story or a poem that has a description of a river in it. Bring it into school and read it to the class. **

15   **Estuaries** Do all the rivers in Britain have estuaries? Find out! ***

A river at work

16   **River poem** You are a river – and you work ever so hard! Do you feel proud of yourself? Or are you a grumbler? Make up a poem about your life. Just one little snag – you must get the words *erode*, *transport* and *deposit* in! **

17   **Design a demonstration** Working in a group, think up a way to demonstrate erosion, transport, and deposition. (Students could vote on the best method – and then the winning group prepares and gives their demonstration.) **/***

18   **Can they cause problems?** Could erosion and deposition by rivers ever cause us problems? Explain. ***

Five landforms created by the river

19   **Rivers on an OS map** Draw a sketch map of a real river and its route, from an OS map (especially if it's a local river). Mark in land height at different points along the river. Mark on features such as meanders, embankments, bridges, etc. ***

20   **The world's highest waterfall** Which is the highest waterfall in the world? Find out, and write a leaflet to persuade tourists to visit it. Your leaflet must include a map! **

21   **A very British gorge** Write a short article for a geography magazine about Cheddar Gorge. Say how it was formed. Don't forget a map showing where it is – and a photo. */**/***

22   **A model river** Working in a group, think up a way to create a 3-D model of a river and its basin, with all the associated landforms. Produce an annotated sketch of the final design, saying what materials you will use and how you'll get the river to flow for the demonstration. (Students can vote on the best design – and produce it.) **/***

23   **River alphabet run** Do an illustrated alphabet run for rivers, with something for each letter. */**/***

Rivers and us

24   **Rivers for pleasure!** Collect photos to show leisure activities in and around rivers. Make a collage of them. *

25   **Who lives there?** Rivers are home to many different forms of wildlife. Find out about one wildlife species that lives in or beside British rivers, and write a report of at least 100 words about it. Don't forget drawings or photos. **

26   **River crossword** Make up a crossword to try out on other students, using what you have learned about rivers so far. **

27 Odd one out Prepare an Odd one out to try out on other students, using what you have learned about rivers so far. **

28 If I had a river … What you do with it? */**/***

Our water supply

29 Where do we get our water supply? Carry out an enquiry to find out where your local water supply comes from. */**/***

30 At the water works Find out exactly what's done to river water to clean it up ready for us to drink. You could present your answer as an annotated drawing, as a two-page article for a geography magazine, or even as a 3-D model. */**/***

31 What happens to our waste water? Carry out an enquiry about what happens to the waste water that goes down the plug holes and loo. Include a diagram of the stages in waste water treatment. (A water company may help – and might even send someone to talk to the class.) */**/***

32 How much? Every household gets a water bill. About how much is it a year, in your area? */**/***

33 How much water do we use? Calculate the water use for your house. (A search on Google for *water calculator UK* will bring up several. Choose one that's at the right level.) */**/***

34 Let's save water! Prepare a leaflet with water-saving tips. (The internet will help.) */**/***

Floods!

35 Recent floods Find out about some recent floods in the UK or elsewhere (but not along the Thames). Prepare a radio report. It should give the name(s) of the country(ies), and the flooding river, and give information about the damage. You can include interviews. **/***

36 Flash floods They can do a great deal of damage. Find out about one example anywhere in the world. Tell the class all about it. **/***

Flooding on the River Thames

37 Interview You are a reporter for the local TV news. You have interviewed the person who lives in the flat in photo B on page 96 of the students' book about the floods. We will call him Mr Adams. Write a full transcript of the interview. In this form:

  Interviewer: Mr Adams, tell me …

  Mr Adams: Well, the first thing I knew …

Say where the interview took place, and add directions for the TV editor, such as when to show Mr Adams, when to cut to pictures of the damage, and when to cut back to you. (Instead, some students could interview the manager of the supermarket in photo C.) **/***

38 Flooding in your home What if your home was flooded to a depth of half a metre? Crawl around on the floor, at home, to investigate what would be damaged. Write a list.

(If you don't live on the ground floor, pretend that you do.) Then see if you can divide your list up into different types of damage, for example, very serious, dangerous, easy to fix, not important. */**/***

39 Flood warning! You receive a phone call from the local flood warning centre. The river is rising and your area will flood. It is not safe to stay in your home. You have one hour to get ready to leave. What you will do in that hour? Write a list – but remember, you've only got an hour to do the things on your list! */**/***

40 What to do after the flood Design a leaflet telling people what to do when they return home after a flood. It must be very clear and simple. For help, try the Environment Agency website at www.environment-agency.gov.uk or write to the nearest Environment Agency office for leaflets. ***

Protecting ourselves from floods

41 Building in the flood plain? You are in charge of planning for Purley-on-Thames. Mr Jamison, a developer, has applied for permission to build a hotel at 662771 on the OS map on page 97 of the students' book. You have discussed his application with your team. Now you are writing to him with your decision and reasons. What will you say? Check the Environment Agency flood risk map for Purley-on-Thames before you reply. See if you can download the map and include it with your answer. **/***

42 Everybody out! Purley-on-Thames is at risk of flooding. Global warming could make floods more frequent and more serious. It's time to air your views.

  a) Write a letter to the *Purley Chronicle* suggesting that everyone just moves out of Purley. Give your reasons – but keep them brief, otherwise the editor will edit them.

  b) Now write a letter from an angry reader of the newspaper in reply to yours. **/***

43 Is your home at risk? Is your home at risk of flooding? Check it out on the Environment Agency flood map (www.environment-agency.gov.uk). **/***

44 It's all our fault? 'The real truth about floods is this: We have built in the wrong places and now we are paying the price.' That is the first sentence of your letter to a national newspaper about the latest floods that caused widespread damage across the UK. Complete the letter! */**/***

45 The amphibious house Find out about the UK's first floating house, built on the Thames at Marlow. Explain how it works. ***

46 Thames Barrier Do some research on the barrier. Think of a really good way to present your findings. */**/***

47 Make up a flood quiz Working in a group, make up a quiz about flooding and quiz other groups. (There could be a prize for the winners.) **

48 Make up a flood crossword Working in a group make up a crossword about flooding. Then swop with another group and complete their crossword. **

6 Africa

Addressing the KS3 Programme of Study

◆ Extend locational knowledge and deepen spatial awareness of the world's countries, using maps of the world to focus on Africa, its environmental regions, key physical and human characteristics, countries, and major cities.

About the content

◆ The chapter opens with a unit on the continents, with the main focus on Africa. This helps to set Africa in its world context, before you move on to look at its countries.

◆ Unit 6.2 outlines Africa's history up to the end of the colonial period. This is included as useful background to the human geography of Africa today.

◆ Most of the units explore atlas-style maps of Africa.

The big picture

These are the key ideas behind this chapter.

◆ Africa is a continent (not a country).

◆ Africa has 54 countries.

◆ In the past, Africa had many empires and kingdoms. But the country borders today are largely a result of the colonisation of Africa by European countries.

◆ The countries are all different. But in terms of human geography, they share many characteristics, such as a high percentage of young people and a high percentage of the workforce in farming.

◆ You can learn a lot about Africa by studying maps.

A students' version of this big picture is given in the *geog.1* students' book opener for Chapter 6, and is the basis of the interactive self-assessment form on *geog.1 Kerboodle*.

The chapter outline

Use this, and their chapter opener, to give students a mental roadmap for the chapter.

6   Africa The chapter opener in the student book is an important part of the chapter; see page 11 for notes about using chapter openers

6.1   What and where is Africa? Africa as one of the world's seven continents

6.2   A little history Africa: the home of the human race … and carved up by European powers

6.3   Africa today About the human geography of Africa

6.4   Africa's countries Explore a map of Africa's countries

6.5   Population distribution in Africa Explore a map of population density, and a table of countries and their populations

6.6   Africa's physical features Explore a map showing relief and the main physical features, with country borders also marked

6.7   Africa's biomes Hot desert, semi-desert, savanna, and rainforest

chapter
overview

Objectives and outcomes for this chapter

Objectives	Unit	Outcomes
Most students will understand:		Most students will be able to:
• that Africa is one of the world's seven continents	6.1, 6.6	• show Africa on an outline map of the world; show the Equator and tropics; name / label the oceans and seas around Africa, and the Suez Canal
• that today's map of Africa is largely shaped by its colonial history	6.2, 6.4	• describe how some European countries took over most of Africa and carved it up among themselves; give one reason why they did this; name at least three of the colonial countries
• that Africa has many countries	6.4	• say that Africa has 54 countries; name at least 12 of them, and their capitals, and say roughly where they are in Africa (e.g. in West Africa)
• that African countries share many characteristics, in terms of their human geography	6.3	• give at least five facts about the human geography of Africa, including the size of its population
• that population distribution is influenced by physical features and climate	6.5	• describe in outline the pattern of population distribution in Africa; give at least two factors that influence the pattern
• that Africa has a variety of physical features	6.6	• name / label at least these, on a map or sketch map of Africa: the Nile; Africa's tallest mountain and largest lake; at least two mountainous regions; three deserts
• that Africa can be divided into four main biomes	6.7	• name the four main biomes; say what the climate is like in each biome; give at least three other facts about each biome

These tie in with the outcomes for each unit in this teacher's handbook, and with 'Your goals for this chapter' in the students' book.

Opportunities for assessment

See the formal assessment materials for this chapter on *geog.1 Kerboodle: Lessons, Resources, and Assessments*. They include an extended assessment task, an exam-style question, end-of-lesson assessments, and a self-assessment form. See also the notes on pages 14–15 of this book.

Getting ready for this chapter

geog.1 Kerboodle contains plans and presentations for each unit, including interactive activities, animations, and worksheets.

About 'Your chapter starter'

The satellite image of Africa on page 100 dramatically shows up the dry areas, with too little rain to support much vegetation. Lake Victoria – Africa's biggest lake by area – shows up clearly, as does its longest river, the Nile. Note the other lakes in East Africa too. Look how close Africa is to Europe, at the southern tip of Spain. (They are 14 km apart.) Point out the triangular Sinai Peninsula. Although it is part of Egypt, it is actually in Asia. Try to ensure that students know where these are: the Mediterranean Sea, the Red Sea, the Gulf of Aden, the Suez Canal, the Strait of Gibraltar.

What and where is Africa?

help at a glance

About this unit

This unit presents a map of the continents, and compares Africa with the others. In 'Your turn', students explore mental images of Africa.

Key points

◆ The world has seven continents.

◆ Africa is a continent (not a country).

◆ Africa is the world's second biggest continent, by area and population.

Key vocabulary

continent

Skills practised in 'Your turn'

◆ Geography skills: q1, explore existing geographical knowledge, and compare answers with a map; q2, q3, interpret tables of data; q4, decide how to display data; q7, interpret a photo

◆ Numeracy skills: q1, keep score; q2, q3, q5, interpret bar charts and other data; q4, display data

◆ Literacy skills: q1, q8, define; q9, compile a spider diagram to summarise

◆ Thinking skills: q7, compare photo with mental images; q8, come up with ways to avoid stereotyped views

Unit outcomes

By the end of this unit most students should be able to:

◆ explain the term given in 'Key vocabulary' above

◆ say that Africa is a continent, not a country

◆ describe where it is, relative to the other continents

◆ point it out on a map of the world

◆ say that it is the second largest continent by both area and population

Ideas for a starter

1 With books closed, ask: How many continents can you name?

2 With books closed, give each student an outline map of Africa. Ask them to write or draw on anything they already know about Africa, add their names, and hand them in. Many students may have stereotypical views about the continent. Use this knowledge to help you broaden their perceptions as the units progress. Repeat the exercise at the very end of the chapter, and compare the results.

3 Discuss: Where in the world is Africa?

4 Ask: What is the capital of Africa? Draw out what is wrong with the question. If necessary, explain that Africa is not a country but a continent of many countries. Ask: Which countries in Africa do you know of? Make a list.

Ideas for plenaries

Plan plenaries for strategic points throughout the lesson, as well as at the end.

Mid-lesson

1 Look at the map on page 102 of the students' book. Ask: Which continents are mainly in the tropics? How do you know?

2 Ask: How much of Africa is within the tropics? Is more of it north, or south, of the Equator? Which continent is Africa furthest from?

End-of-lesson

3 Ask students to draw a rough sketch of the outline of Africa and mark in the Equator and oceans?

4 Ask: What would you like to know about Africa?

5 Ask: How many times do you think the British Isles would fit into the continent of Africa? Have a guess! (Answer: 131.5 times)

6 Display a range of photos of different places in Africa that may not match stereotypes. Ask: Which photos are of Africa? Explain that they all are! Explore which images surprised students, and why. Recap on the meaning of *stereotype*. Ask: How can you ensure that your views of other parts of the world are not based on stereotypes?

Further class and homework opportunities

Suggestions 1–6 on page 140 of this book

geog.1 workbook, page 53

geog.1 Kerboodle: see lesson presentation, worksheets, and end-of-lesson assessment

Answers to 'Your turn'

1 a A continent is a large landmass plus its associated islands. A continent is divided up into political entities called countries. (Antarctica is an exception: although seven countries lay claim to it, it is not officially divided up.)

b, c Students could also check their list against the one on page 108 in the students' book. However there is also value in finding the countries on a map. You could ask who got most marks.

2 All are true.

3 All are true.

4 A bar chart is a straightforward way to display the information. For a pictogram, students could draw seven identical containers (e.g. squares), each representing an area of 1 square km. They should label each with the name of a continent, and add an overall heading. They then mark in the appropriate number of stick figures or dots in each container, to represent people.

5 A false; B true; C true

6 a Indian Ocean

b Atlantic Ocean

c X is near the Equator, where the Sun shines strongly. Some students may correctly refer to X as being in the tropics.

7 a Expect TV news / films, newspapers / magazines, parents / friends, appeals from charities.

b This photo shows lots of modern high-rise buildings and green spaces. Students may well be surprised.

8 a Where people have fixed views or opinions about something, which do not reflect reality; usually they have accepted them from other sources, without thinking.

b Answers may include: visit Africa; search the internet and look at lots of photos, and read widely about Africa; speak to people who have been there or lived there.

9 Spider map headings could include: people, countries, climate, physical features, biomes. Encourage students to use their prior knowledge to add notes.

About this unit

This unit outlines Africa's history, from ancient times until the end of the colonial era.

Key points

◆ Our species (*Homo sapiens*) emerged in Africa about 200 000 years ago. Groups of us began to leave Africa about 60 000 years ago.

◆ Africa has a long history of civilisations, empires, and kingdoms.

◆ Portuguese explorers arrived in West Africa in the 15th century, and began to trade; they were followed over time by traders from other European countries.

◆ The Europeans wanted slaves, as well as gold, ivory, and other materials. Slave trading was already common in parts of Africa. But with the arrival of the Europeans, it became a major feature of Africa's economy.

◆ Europe's part in the slave trade lasted from the 15th century until it was finally banned among European countries around 1850.

◆ While the slave trade was collapsing, the Europeans were already colonising parts of Africa. The main era of colonisation was from about 1814 to 1905.

◆ In 1884, the European colonial powers met in Germany to agree a new map of Africa.

◆ The colonies gradually gained their independence, from 1951 to 1980. (Since then, several countries have broken up further.)

Key vocabulary

Homo sapiens, slave trade, plantation, colonise, colony, independence

Skills practised in 'Your turn'

◆ Geography skills: q2, q4, q5, interpret maps

◆ Literacy skills: q1, q3, comprehension; q7, define

◆ Thinking skills: q6, q7, explain; q8, think of negative consequences

Unit outcomes

By the end of this unit most students should be able to:

◆ explain the terms given in 'Key vocabulary' above

◆ explain why all of us (*Homo sapiens*) are linked to Africa

◆ name at least one ancient African civilisation, empire, or kingdom

◆ explain what the Atlantic slave trade was

◆ say that a number of European countries between them colonised most of Africa, and name at least three of them

◆ say that the African countries gained independence from 1951 onwards

Ideas for a starter

1 Recap on Africa's vital statistics. See if students can remember key facts about Africa such as it's being the second largest continent, by both population and area, with 54 countries.

2 Recap: What's the difference between a country and a continent? Ask students to sort these places into countries and continents: Europe, India, UK, Africa, North America, Morocco, Canada, Asia. Challenge them to match each country to its continent.

3 Say: Everyone in this room has a connection with Africa. What is it? Then turn to the map on page 13 of the students' book.

Ideas for plenaries

Plan plenaries for strategic points throughout the lesson, as well as at the end.

Mid-lesson

1 Explore the pictures on page 104 of the student book. (The illustration of Mansa Musa is from a Spanish map of 1375.) Ask: Who appears to have the power in the picture of the Kingdom of Kongo?

2 Ask: Where does ivory come from? Why do you think the Europeans wanted it? What do you think were the problems – and consequences – of sourcing it?

3 Ask: Why exactly did Europeans want slaves? What and where were the plantations? Who owned them?

4 Ask for comments about Elmina Castle, in the photo on page 105 of the students' book. Why was it built in that place? What else can you say about it?

End-of-lesson

5 Use 'Your turn' question 8 as a plenary. Prompt forward thinking: Do you think the consequences of colonisation might still be apparent in African countries today?

6 Does any country have a right to colonise another?

7 Write a set of statements on the board in jumbled order, giving events in Africa's history. Include for example *the evolution of Homo sapiens, the rise and fall of Ancient Egypt*, and *the first Portuguese traders arrive*. Ask students to put them in chronological order.

8 Explore: What do you think it felt like to be captured as a slave, then traded and transported to the other side of the world to work on a plantation for the rest of your life?

Further class and homework opportunities

Suggestions 7–12 on page 140 of this book

geog.1 workbook, page 54

geog.1 Kerboodle: see lesson presentation, worksheets, and end-of-lesson assessment

Answers to 'Your turn'

1 It is where the human race began. Experts think that the first human species appeared in East Africa (in Ethiopia) about 2 million years ago, and we (*Homo sapiens*) emerged around 200 000 years ago.

2 The Nile

3 Both made money from ivory, metals, and slaves.

4 Britain and France

5 Gambia (hard to see on a small map), Sierra Leone, Ghana, Nigeria, part of Libya, Egypt, Sudan and South Sudan, part of Somalia, Kenya, Uganda, Malawi, Zambia, Zimbabwe, Botswana, Swaziland, Lesotho, South Africa. (Note that after the Second World War, Britain took control of Tanzania and part of Cameroon, which had been German colonies.)

6 Expect students to refer to the desire for resources (e.g. timber, gold and other metals, and crops). Some may refer to a wish to become a world power with global outposts. (European countries controlled areas of Africa much larger than themselves.) Some may mention slaves, however the

slave trade had been banned in many European countries and was largely over by the start of the main era of colonisation (about 1814–1905).

7 a In this context, being exploited means being made use of by the colonisers, to benefit themselves. 'Fought for their independence' means they fought to throw out the colonisers and rule themselves.

b Students could mention: the wish to control and benefit from their own resources; fed up with being treated as inferior; fed up with living in poverty while the colonisers profited from the resources; the wish to have education and better health care (like the colonisers).

8 Tensions between groups with different customs and religious beliefs; disputes over land split by borders; loyalty to groups across the border, rather than within the country; different languages, causing poor communication; power struggles between different groups for control. Even today, many of the problems in African countries arise from rivalries between different ethnic groups.

Africa today

help at a glance

About this unit

This unit gives an overview of Africa and its people today.

Key points

♦ Today Africa has 54 countries, 23 of them smaller in area than the UK. (The number changes as new countries such as South Sudan, form.)

♦ These are characteristics of Africa:

 – a young, rapidly growing population

 – a high percentage of the workforce in farming

 – a high percentage of people living in poverty

 – many ethnic groups, and many languages

 – English is the official language in over 20 countries.

♦ Africa can earn money from its mineral resources, and agriculture.

♦ Africa's big challenge is to end poverty.

Key vocabulary

ethnic groups, official language

Skills practised in 'Your turn'

♦ Geography skills: q8, interpret a photo

♦ Numeracy skills: q7, interpret life expectancy data

♦ Thinking skills: q1, assess facts; q3, predict problems; q4, suggest advantages and disadvantages; q6, respond to an opinion; q7, think of factors that influence life expectancy, suggest reasons

Unit outcomes

By the end of this unit most students should be able to:

♦ explain the terms given in 'Key vocabulary' above

♦ state the number of countries in Africa today

♦ give at least five facts about Africa's people (including size of population)

♦ say that Africa has many resources

♦ say that African countries are working to put an end to poverty

Ideas for a starter

1 Display NASA's satellite image of the world at night. (It can be found on various internet sites.) Ask: Why is lots of Africa dark? Is it because there are not many people? Explain that this will be explored later.

2 Ask: What languages do people speak in Africa? Say they'll find out later!

3 Find some typical Kora music on the internet. Introduce it: Music and dance have been part of African cultures for centuries. There is no typical African music but many different instruments and styles. The Kora is a 21-stringed instrument from West Africa. It takes great skill to play it. Ask students to relax, close their eyes and listen to the music. Ask: What images came into your mind when you listened?

4 Take in a variety of foods or other products imported from Africa, and help students to find out where they came from. Ask students to find those places on the map of Africa.

Ideas for plenaries

Plan plenaries for strategic points throughout the lesson, as well as at the end.

Mid-lesson

1   Ask students to read aloud the text below the photos, on page 106 of the students' book.

2   Say: Africa is rich in natural resources. What exactly does that mean? Is it a good thing or a bad thing? Explain.

End-of-lesson

3   Debate: Some Africans are rich and many live comfortably, but almost half live in great poverty. We all have the same basic needs. What do you think all humans need, to live a comfortable life?

4   Ask students to tell you three interesting facts about Africa, which they met for the first time today.

5   Ask: So who'd like to visit Africa? Why?

Further class and homework opportunities

Suggestions 13–17 on page 140 of this book

geog.1 workbook, page 55

geog.1 Kerboodle: see lesson presentation, worksheets, and end-of-lesson assessment

Answers to 'Your turn'

1   Answers will vary.

2   Around 1.1 billion

3   Expect students to refer to the rapid rise in demand for food, shelter, drinking water, fuel, schools, health services, and employment, which a country may not be able to meet. Levels of overcrowding, disease, crime, pollution, and damage to the environment are all likely to rise.

4   Advantages: you could expect a young population to be lively, and healthy, with lots of new ideas. As children reach working age, there will be plenty of people available to work.

   Disadvantages: half the population under 20 also means a high percentage who are too young to work, who need to be looked after and educated. There may not be enough schools, doctors, etc. There may not be enough mature people to support and direct them. When they reach working age, there may not be enough work for them to do. And when they have children of their own, the population will rise fast, giving the problems in answer 3 above.

5   They were British colonies. Now more people speak English as a second language than any local language; so English allows them to communicate more easily.

6   Students may understand the need for people to cut off all links with the colonists, and rediscover their own languages and identity. However, English is widely spoken around the world. It is the official language of more countries than any other. Being able to speak English makes trade and travel easier. Abandoning it might be a mistake.

7   a   Students may refer to a healthy diet; good medical care; a clean water supply; exercise; low crime rates; the opportunity to earn a living; wealth; a clean and unpolluted environment; a comfortable home; a supportive family; perhaps even the smoking ban in enclosed public spaces.

    b   Those two countries are not well off and many of the things listed in answer 7a, such as a good medical care and a clean water supply, cost money. So many people in those countries won't have them and are likely to die younger.

8   a   They show the start and end points of the diamond trade.

    b   All the work appears to be done by hand. There is no sign of machinery to cut the straight banks, so that is probably done by hand too. People are standing in muddy water, and on muddy slopes, with no protective clothing. It must get very hot when the Sun is blazing down.

About this unit

This unit explores Africa's countries, capital cities, and regions.

Key points

◆ Today, Africa has 54 countries. (Many are the result of the carving up of Africa by European colonisers.)

◆ Africa consists of five regions – North, West, East, Central, and Southern Africa.

Key vocabulary

(No new vocabulary)

Skills practised in 'Your turn'

◆ Geography skills: q1–q6, interpret a map, and find countries and cities on it; q5, compare two maps, to match countries to regions; q6, interpret a photo, and draw a sketch from it

Unit outcomes

By the end of this unit most students should be able to:

◆ name at least 12 African countries and their capitals, and say roughly where in Africa they are (e.g. in West Africa)

Ideas for a starter

1 With books closed, ask: How many African countries can you name? List them on the board. When no one can think of any others, say: Now turn to page 108 of the students' book!

2 With books closed, write up the names of some African countries – but all jumbled up. Who will be first to unjumble them?

3 Display photographs or play film clips from several African countries to give an overview of their diversity (e.g. from http://www.7billionothers.org/testimonies).

Ideas for plenaries

Plan plenaries for strategic points throughout the lesson, as well as at the end.

Mid-lesson

1 Ask: Why do you think there is such a big difference in the size of countries in Africa? Can you think why colonisers didn't carve up some of the big ones? (Perhaps some were viewed as useless because of desert or thick forest?)

2 Ask: Why do you think so many small countries are clustered on the west coast of Africa, near the Equator? (This was where most of the colonisers arrived first; it was a source of gold and slaves, so the colonisers fought over any patches they could.)

3 Display the outline of several African countries. Ask students to identify them from the shape, or locate them on the map. Ask: What are the neighbouring countries? How many landlocked countries are there on the African continent?

4 Guess the country: One student chooses a country and, without naming it, gives clues to its identity and position. When another student guesses the name, they then choose another country, and the game continues.

End-of-lesson

5 Ask: Which country in Africa, would you most like to visit and why? Ask volunteers to present their chosen country to the rest of the class.

6 Ask students to imagine it is 1884. European colonial powers meet in Berlin divide Africa into countries, which they allocate between themselves. Say: Some of your family and friends live on one side of a new border and some on the other. So you now live in different countries, ruled by different European powers, who speak different languages. What impact will it have on you? How do you feel about it?

7 Ask students to complete these sentences about this unit:
  – The most interesting thing I found out was …
  – I was surprised to learn that …
  – I would like to know more about …

Further class and homework opportunities

Suggestions 18–26 on page 141 of this book

geog.1 workbook, page 56

geog.1 Kerboodle: see lesson presentation, worksheets, and end-of-lesson assessment

Answers to 'Your turn'

1 a Kenya b Lesotho c Madagascar
  d Niger e Togo

2 a Madagascar, Malawi, Mali, Mauritania, Morocco, Mozambique, (Mauritius not shown)
  b Zambia, Zimbabwe
  c Lesotho, Liberia, Libya
  d São Tomé and Príncipe, Senegal, Sierra Leone, Somalia, South Africa, South Sudan, Sudan, Swaziland, (Seychelles not shown)

3 Morocco, Algeria, Libya, Egypt, Western Sahara, Mauritania, Mali, Niger, Chad, Sudan, Angola, Zambia, Namibia, Botswana, South Africa, Tanzania, Kenya, Somalia, Ethiopia

4 The countries are:
  a Ethiopia b Zambia c Kenya
  d Libya e Mauritania f Uganda
  g Namibia h Gabon

5 a Any three of: Equatorial Guinea, Gabon, Congo, Democratic Republic of Congo, Central African Republic

  b Any four of: Western Sahara, Morocco, Algeria, Tunisia, Libya, Egypt
  c Any three of: Sudan, South Sudan, Ethiopia, Eritrea, Djibouti, Somalia, Uganda, Rwanda, Burundi, Tanzania, Kenya
  d Any four of: Mauritania, Mali, Niger, Chad, Senegal, The Gambia, Guinea Bissau, Guinea, Sierra Leone, Liberia, Côte d'Ivoire, Ghana, Togo, Benin, Burkina, Nigeria, Cameroon
  e Any four of: Angola, Zambia, Malawi, Mozambique, Zimbabwe, Botswana, Namibia, South Africa, Lesotho, Swaziland

6 a Egypt
  b It looks wealthy, with modern skyscrapers, a large river, trees, parks and/or sports grounds, a mosque, boats of different kinds including the felucca with the white sail, several bridges. The city extends into the distance and looks large. It's a calm day (the river surface is smooth), with a haze in the air.
  c Labels on the sketch could include most of the points covered in answer 6b; the river is the Nile.

About this unit

This unit looks at the population distribution in Africa, through a map and a table of data.

Key points

◆ The population of Africa is about 1.1 billion.

◆ Population density is the number of people living in a place, per square kilometre.

◆ Population density varies across Africa. (It is influenced by physical features, and climate.)

◆ Of the 54 African countries, 26 have a smaller population than London.

Key vocabulary

population, population density

Skills practised in 'Your turn'

◆ Geography skills: q4, q5, q7, interpret a map of population density; q7, compare maps to explain patterns of population density; q8, interpret a photo

◆ Numeracy skills: q2, analyse a table of data; q5, complete and analyse a table of data; q8, interpret a line graph

◆ Literacy skills: q1, define; q6, comment on data, in at least 50 words

◆ Thinking skills: q3, q7, q8, explain; q8, deduce from what's shown in a photo

Unit outcomes

By the end of this unit most students should be able to:

◆ explain the terms given in 'Key vocabulary' above

◆ interpret a map of population density (a choropleth map)

◆ describe the pattern of population density in Africa

◆ give at least two factors that influence the pattern

◆ use tables of data more competently

Ideas for a starter

1   Ask: What does *population density* mean? Is the population in Africa likely to be spread equally across the continent? Why / Why not?

2   Display NASA's satellite image of the world at night (it can be found on various internet sites) and explore Africa together. Draw attention to high concentrations of light along the Nile, in West Africa, and around the north coast of Africa. Draw out that this shows areas of high pop density.

3   Whacky facts: In 2001, a 36-year-old Nigerian school teacher won an award for inventing a method to refrigerate food without electricity. He designed a 'pot-in-pot' system, putting one smaller clay pot inside a larger one and separating the two with sand that was kept damp. The evaporation of water from the sand causes the inner pot to cool and keeps food fresh for longer. (You could download images of the pot-in-pot.)

Ideas for plenaries

Plan plenaries for strategic points throughout the lesson, as well as at the end.

Mid-lesson

1 Ask questions about the map on page 110 of the students' book, to check that students can interpret it. What are the purple lines? The deepest orange patches? The palest patches? The yellow squares? The black squares? The other black dots?

2 Use 'Your turn' question 2 as a plenary. Draw out that almost half of Africa's countries have a population lower than London's, and few have more people than the UK.

3 Point out that Egypt has more people than the UK, yet most of the country is empty. Ask: Can you explain this? Where is everyone?

4 Look at the photos of Lagos on page 111 of the students' book. Ask: What can you tell about Lagos from the photos? Do you know anything else about it?

End-of-lesson

5 Imagine this. Your family is not well off, so you decide to try your luck in Africa's biggest city. You move from a village in rural Nigeria to Lagos. Write to your friend back home. Say what you think of Lagos so far. Describe where you are living. Do you miss the village?

6 Ask: What was the most surprising thing you learned today?

Further class and homework opportunities

Suggestion 27 on page 141 of this book

geog.1 workbook, page 57

geog.1 Kerboodle: see lesson presentation, worksheets, and end-of-lesson assessment

Answers to 'Your turn'

1 a The number of people living in a place
   b The average number of people living in a place per square kilometre

2 a Seychelles   b Nigeria
   c Democratic Republic of Congo, Egypt, Ethiopia, Nigeria
   d There are 26!

3 The figures are approximate: the countries may not have had a proper census, since it may be hard to carry one out in rural areas. The figures also change continually, as a result of births and deaths. (So *all* population figures are approximate to some degree.)

4 a Allow leeway with answers! Reasonable answers: Rwanda, Burundi, Nigeria, Gambia, Uganda, Malawi.
   b Again allow leeway. Reasonable answers: Western Sahara, Namibia, Mauritania, Botswana, Libya.

5 Somalia 15, Namibia 3, Nigeria 188

6 The UK has the highest population density of the four countries. The satellite image on page 100 of the students' book might help to explain why the figures for Namibia and Somalia are so low. Meanwhile, much of the UK is built up, with many cities and towns, so it has a high population density. (Explain that Nigeria has almost 2.5 times more people than the UK, but it is around 3.8 times larger in area. So it is less crowded.)

7 a The Tropic of Cancer passes through the Sahara Desert. Not many people live there because there is not enough rain to grow crops. (Some people do live in oases, and also along the River Nile, where fields are irrigated.)

   b People settle along coasts because of access to the sea for fishing, and for trade with other places. Ports develop where ships can anchor safely.
   c The lakes are a source of fresh water for drinking and washing. They also offer fishing and transport by boat for trade.
   d The wiggly strip follows the course of the River Nile. People use its water to irrigate fields for growing crops, and the land is very fertile. (They can also fish on the Nile and travel by boat for trade.)

8 a About 4 million
   b About 10 million
   c To escape conditions that are common in rural areas in Nigeria and other African countries: poverty, unemployment, poor schools and health care, and poor access to clean water or electricity. Some people hope for an exciting city life.
   d More homes, hospitals, schools, doctors, teachers, and police will be needed to cope with the extra people. They will need food, water, and electricity supplies. The transport systems may not be able to cope. There will be more sewage and refuse to dispose of.
   e Rubbish lying around, and animal waste, are a health hazard (especially for young children). The shacks are unlikely to have running water or toilets, so you'll fetch water from a public tap and use public toilets / latrines (if there are any). But at least some places have electricity. You'd have to find a fence or rail to hang your washing on. Imagine what the place is like after heavy rain!

Africa's physical features

help at a glance

About this unit

This unit looks at Africa's key physical features.

Key points

- ◆ Africa has a wide variety of physical features, as you'd expect from a continent.
- ◆ They include Earth's longest river (the Nile), its largest hot desert (the Sahara), its second largest freshwater lake, by area (Lake Victoria), and its largest sheet of falling water (Victoria Falls).
- ◆ East and Southern Africa are the most mountainous regions.
- ◆ Mt Kilimanjaro is Africa's highest mountain.
- ◆ East Africa has the most lakes.

Key vocabulary

desert, plateau, highlands, gulf (all on map)

Skills practised in 'Your turn'

- ◆ Geography skills: q1–q9, interpret a map; q9, obtain information by comparing two maps; q9, practise drawing and labelling a rough map of Africa
- ◆ Numerical skills: q7, pick out second and third largest numbers
- ◆ Thinking skills: q6, come up with a reason

Unit outcomes

By the end of this unit most students should be able to:

- ◆ explain the terms given in 'Key vocabulary' above
- ◆ interpret a choropleth map showing relief and main physical features
- ◆ say, at least roughly, where these physical features are in Africa:
  - – the Sahara and two other deserts
  - – the Nile and at least two other rivers
  - – Mt Kilimanjaro and three other areas of high land
  - – Lake Victoria
- ◆ point out where these are, relative to Africa: the Atlantic Ocean, the Indian Ocean, the Red Sea, the Mediterranean Sea, the Suez Canal, the Equator, the Tropics of Cancer and Capricorn

Ideas for a starter

1 Ask students to close their eyes, and say: Imagine that behind you is a vast continent. To the east is the warm, tropical Indian Ocean with its coral reefs; to the west stretches the great Atlantic. You can snorkel in one and surf in the other. To the south, the water stretches all the way to the cold Antarctic. Where do you think you might be? (On the southern tip of Africa, at Cape L'Agulhas, where the two oceans meet and mingle)

2 With books closed, ask: What does *Africa's physical features* mean? Who can name some of them? List them on the board.

Ideas for plenaries

Plan plenaries for strategic points throughout the lesson, as well as at the end.

Mid-lesson

1   Explore the map together. Which are the highest places? And the lowest? (The Qattara Depression is shown, but Lake Assal, which is not shown, is lower.) What can students say about the main rivers? Explore the meaning of *gulf*, as in the Gulf of Aden.

2   Point out that although the Kalahari is called a desert, it is really semi-desert, with enormous areas of vegetation after rain. Support this with photos from the internet, or look back at the satellite image on page 100 of the students' book.

3   Compare satellite image of Africa on page 100 with the physical map on page 112.

4   After students have done 'Your turn' question 1, ask them to write a short descriptive paragraph about the River Nile. Prompt: What else do you know about the Nile from other units (e.g. population density and distribution, ancient civilisations)?

End-of-lesson

5   With books closed, ask students to name the areas of water off Africa's coast.

6   Ask students to justify this statement: Africa is a continent of geographical contrasts.

Further class and homework opportunities

Suggestions 28–29 on page 141 of this book

geog.1 workbook, page 58

geog.1 Kerboodle: see lesson presentation, worksheets, and end-of-lesson assessment

Answers to 'Your turn'

1   a   River Nile   b   North
    c   Blue Nile – Ethiopian Highlands; White Nile – Lake Victoria (not so easy to identify as the source on a map of this size)
    d   i   Mediterranean Sea
        ii It splits into small rivers, like the fingers on a hand. (This is the Nile Delta.)

2   Students may confuse main rivers with their tributaries. Point out that the main river is the longest one. Answers: Congo, Niger, Senegal, Cunene, Orange.

3   a   Zambezi   b   False

4   Rift Valley

5   a   East Africa: it has the largest total area of land above 2000 m (the deepest shade); it has Africa's four highest mountains. The Ethiopian Highlands form the largest continuous area of high altitude in all of Africa. (Students may need reminding about how far 'East Africa' extends. See the map on page 109 of the students' book.)
    b   In north west Africa
    c   Accept two from: Hoggar Mountains, Tibesti Mountains, Ethiopian Highlands, Angola Plateau (a high plateau), and Drakensberg (a high escarpment).

6   a   Mt Kilimanjaro
    b   The higher you go, the colder it gets. At the top, it is high enough for glaciers. (The gas molecules in the air transfer heat energy. It gets colder with altitude because the number of gas molecules in the air decreases.)

7   Mt Kenya 5200 m, Mt Ruwenzori 5120 m

8   a   Sahara Desert   b   North Africa
    c   It is generally flat but it has two areas of higher land, the Hoggar Mountains and the Tibesti Mountains.
    d   Namibia Desert, Kalahari Desert. But note that the Kalahari is semi-desert rather than true desert. After rains it has huge areas of vegetation.

9   The ship sails through the Gulf of Aden. Then it sails along the Red Sea, passing Djibouti, Eritrea, Sudan, and Egypt. It passes through Egypt's Suez Canal and into the Mediterranean Sea, and heads for the Strait of Gibraltar. It passes the coastlines of northern Egypt, Libya, Tunisia, Algeria, and northern Morocco, before entering the Atlantic Ocean at the Strait of Gibraltar. It then swings north towards the UK. A very exciting journey!

10 Help students to develop a simple but acceptable shape for Africa. For example, the lower section is like a downward-pointing triangle with a 'rounded' point.

About this unit

This unit looks at Africa's four main biomes, and their characteristics.

Key points

◆ Africa has different climate zones, and these in turn lead to different biomes.

◆ A biome is a large region with the same type of climate throughout, and with distinctive species of plants and animals that have adapted to this climate.

◆ Africa has four main biomes: hot desert, semi-desert, savanna, and rainforest.

◆ Hot deserts are very hot in the day, very cold at night, and have very little rain.

◆ The semi-desert is a bit cooler than the desert, with some rain.

◆ The savanna is warm all year, with wet and dry seasons.

◆ The rainforest is warm and wet all year.

Key vocabulary

biome, hot desert, semi-desert, savanna, rainforest

Skills practised in 'Your turn'

◆ Geography skills: q2–q4, interpret a biome map, and compare it with a country map; q6, identify the pattern in a map; q7, compare a map and a satellite image; q8, compare biome and population patterns; q9, interpret photos

◆ Literacy skills: q1, q4, define

◆ Thinking skills: q3, predict consequences; q5, q8, explain; q9, give reasons

Unit outcomes

By the end of this unit most students should be able to:

◆ explain the terms given in 'Key vocabulary' above

◆ name the four main biomes in Africa

◆ say roughly where the four biomes are, on a map of Africa, and describe the overall pattern relative to the Equator

◆ describe the climate of each biome

◆ give at least three other facts about each biome

Ideas for a starter

1 From Kerboodle, and with books closed, look again at the satellite image from page 100 of the students' book. Ask questions such as: Where does it look as if vegetation is growing?

2 Write the word *biome* on the board. Ask: What does this term mean? Any suggestions?

3 Show a selection of photos from Africa's four biomes. For example, the Namib Desert, rainforest in the Congo, the Ogaden in Ethiopia, a game park in Kenya. Include people and animals if possible. The environments all look very different. Why? (Rainfall is the main factor.)

4 Display photos of Africa's physical landscapes, to show the rich diversity and beauty of the continent. Ask: Which landscapes surprised you? Why? Is it greener than you thought it would be? Is it more diverse?

Ideas for plenaries

Plan plenaries for strategic points throughout the lesson, as well as at the end.

Mid-lesson

1 Ask: If all its rainforest is cut down, do you think Africa will still have a rainforest biome? If not, what do you think it might have instead?

2 Ask: Do you think people can live in a hot desert? What kind of lifestyle is possible? What problems would they have?

End-of-lesson

3 Rainfall is the main factor that makes Africa's biomes so different. Download a rainfall map for Africa. Ask students to compare it with the map of page 114 of the students' book, and the satellite image on page 100. What do they notice?

4 Display photos of different environments in Africa. Ask students to write down three adjectives for each. Build a list on the board, to show the huge variety.

5 If you did starter 2 in Unit 6.1, repeat it now. Compare students' responses. Assess how attitudes to and perceptions of Africa have changed.

Further class and homework opportunities

Suggestions 30–35 on page 141 of this book

geog.1 workbook, page 59

geog.1 Kerboodle: see lesson presentation, worksheets, and end-of-lesson assessment

Answers to 'Your turn'

1 A biome is a large region with roughly the same type of climate, plants, and animals, throughout. The plants and animals have adapted to the climate.

2 a It is too dry for most plants, and also very windy.

b The plants grow close to the ground; they have long roots to reach down to water; thick stems for storing water; spines instead of leaves to reduce water loss (and to keep animals at bay).

c See the map.

3 a Note: the Sahel borders the Sahara, and does not include the semi-desert areas in the Horn of Africa.

b The lack of rain leads to a water shortage (drought). Crops die, so neither animals nor humans can get enough to eat – and they don't have enough water to drink. They may die.

4 a Savanna

b Lions, elephants, giraffes, zebra, gazelles – and many others!

c Any five from the large number of countries that lie at least partly in this biome.

d Desertification is the process of turning land into desert, often through overuse.

5 a Rainforest

b All year round this biome is warm, with plentiful sunlight and moisture; these conditions promote photosynthesis.

6 The pattern from north to south, and curling at the bottom towards the south west, is: desert, semi-desert, savanna, rainforest, savanna, semi-desert (the Kalahari), desert (the Namib). The Equator forms the axis of the pattern.

7 There is a good match in some places, but not others.

• The desert and semi-desert areas on the map show up as gold and orange on the satellite image.

• The rainforest in Central Africa shows up as deep green. But in other places on the satellite image there is little or no deep green because the rainforest has been largely destroyed! Look along the southern coast of West Africa, for example, and at the Ethiopian Highlands. Most of this destruction occurred in the last 50 or 60 years.

• The savanna shows up as a lighter thinner green. Look at the lower parts of Central and East Africa. This suggests that the satellite image was taken during or at the end of a rainy season, when vegetation in the savanna flourishes.

8 a i Desert

ii It is too dry to grow crops, and they won't grow in sand, and there's not enough water for animals and people.

b i The rainforest biome is densely populated in places, for example, along the south coast of West Africa where there are several major cities, and in the Ethiopian Highlands. It is less densely populated in other places.

ii Where the rainforest biome is densely populated, it means that the forest has been destroyed. The satellite image confirms this. People are living in the other areas of the rainforest biome too, for example, in Central Africa. But population density is mostly quite low (1–10 people per sq km). Many are likely to be farmers who cleared patches of forest to farm.

c i Savanna. Students will find this hard to answer. Suggest that they check the map key on page 110 of the students' book, and look for the biome with most cities.

ii Of the four, savanna is the biome most suited to farming. Although people do clear rainforest for farmland, the soil is poor and quickly becomes exhausted.

9 Answers will vary.

Most of these suggestions are addressed to your students. Where research or further resources are needed, the internet will almost certainly provide the answer.

The suggestions are graded *, **, *** according to level of difficulty. Some are suitable for all levels, and can be differentiated by outcome.

What and where is Africa?

1   **World wordsearch** Create a wordsearch on the continents and oceans. Swap, and do your partner's. */**

2   **Continent bingo** Create a bingo sheet with seven rows of squares (or six rows, if you don't want to include Antarctica), say five or six squares in a row. Label each row with the name of a continent. Give a sheet to each small team of students. At regular (short) intervals, call out a number and then a name, for example, the name of a country, capital city, famous tourist attraction, continent-specific animal (such as penguin, Indian tiger), international football team, or a continent-specific phrase such as *South Pole*. Students write the numbers in the appropriate rows, one in each square, while you also keep track. The first group to fill all the rows correctly wins. */**/***

3   **Ocean bingo** Do the same as 2 above for the oceans. You could call out names of countries or cities that border them. Let students work with atlases to find the answers, perhaps allowing more time. ***

4   **Did you see?** A student takes the hot seat, chooses a continent, and says he or she has visited everywhere there. Other students open their atlases and fire 'Did you visit X?' questions at the target student, where X is a country on that continent, or not. After say ten questions, or three wrong answers, the student is replaced. When the student gives a wrong answer, the questioner must explain why it is wrong. For example: Vietnam is in Asia, not Africa. (Russia and Turkey may cause problems, since they straddle continents.) ***

5   **Old maps of the world** The map of the world was not always like the one on page 102 of the students' book. Find some images of old maps, and display them. ***

6   **Google Earth** Explore the continents on Google Earth, without any labels turned on, and then with the lowest level of labelling. Turn Earth this way and that! */**/***

A little history

7   **What were the three stages of the Atlantic slave trade?** The shipping of slaves from Africa to North America was one stage of the slave trade. Find out about all three stages. Show them on a map, with notes about each stage. **/***

8   **Read aloud** Find a novel about slavery. (Your English teacher will help.) Find a passage about the everyday life of a slave, and read it aloud to the class. **

9   **Did America have a colony in Africa?** Find out how Liberia, in West Africa, came to be. Do you think it counts as an ex-colony? ***

10 **Does the slave trade matter to you?** Do you think the slave trade has touched your life in any way at all? Think! Tell your conclusions, with reasons. **/***

11 **Why is Elmina Castle in that place?** Find out about its history. */**/***

12 **The road to independence** It's less than 40 years since the last African country gained independence. Think up an interesting way to show the timeline for independence. Perhaps hang cards from a string across the classroom, with the country names, flags, date of independence. It could be colour-coded by coloniser. Agree a format and do one or two cards each, then put them all in order. */**/***

Africa today

13 **Africa wall display** Collect as many interesting and varied images of Africa as you can. Find a way to group them, for example, by physical features, people, towns and cities, wild animals. *

14 **GDP per capita** This gives you an idea of how well off people in a place are, *on average*. It is found by adding up how much everyone in the place earns in a year, and dividing it by the number of people in the place. It is always given in dollars. Here are some figures for 2010, for the continents.

Continent	GDP per capita
Oceania	39 000
North America	32 000
Europe	25 000
South America	9 000
Asia	2 900
Africa	1 600

Use Excel or a similar program to draw a bar chart for this data. Then add notes to it to explain what it shows. What can you say about Africa compared with other continents? How many times better off are Europeans than Africans, on average? Is everyone in Africa really poor? **/***

15 **Draw a pie chart** … showing the percentage of the world population in each continent. You could draw it by hand or in Excel. **/***

16 **African connections** Think about your connections with Africa. Have you been there? Do you have relatives there? Or friends from there? Do you eat anything grown in Africa? See how many connections you can come up with. Find a way to display them (perhaps around a drawing of you). Check page 13 of the students' book too! */**/***

17 **A famous African** Choose a famous African, alive or dead. Create a display on an A4 sheet about him or her, or prepare a piece for a website. See if you can choose someone different from everyone else in the class. Make your choice interesting! Write at least 100 words! */**/***

Africa's countries

18 Adopt an African country You are a geography detective. What geographical questions would you ask about a country you'd never been to? Agree a set of questions with the class, and a way to present the answers. Then choose an African country, or your teacher will allocate one. To your answers, add two very interesting or unusual facts you discovered about the country. */**/***

19 Africa in the news Make a note of all references to African countries in the news this week, in a newspaper or on TV. Find a way to display the references (perhaps as speech bubbles linked to a blank political map of Africa, with the country shaded). Overall, is the news positive? */**/***

20 Africa wordsearch Make up a wordsearch for the names of African countries. See how many you can fit in. Then put it with an outline political map of Africa (with the country boundaries marked on). Give it to a partner. The partner has to find each name, then shade and label that country on the map (preferably without looking at a reference map – or else use the map on page 108 of the students' book). */**/***

21 Colour me quick Give out outline political maps of Africa. A student calls out a country name. Everyone else shades and labels it on their outline maps (with help from the map on page 108 of the students' book). Allow only a short time for this. Then another student calls out a country name. This continues until all the countries are shaded and labelled. If a student calls out a name that was used already, he or she forfeits that turn. */**/***

22 Place quiz Choose a country or city in Africa. Without naming it, write down five facts about it to tell the rest of the class. The class has to identify the country or city. (This could be a game. Students take turns to present their facts. Award 1 point to the student who identifies a place first, and 1 to any student whose place is not identified. At the end of each turn, the 'winner' marks the place on a large outline map of Africa.) **/***

23 A hard snap Make a pack of cards, with the names of African countries on half of the cards and their capitals on the other half. Devise a way to play Snap! **/***

24 Fiendish anagrams Make up a set of anagrams of say five or six African countries (or use an anagram generator on the internet). See how long it takes for the class to work them out. **/***

25 A musical treat Find some African music, by African musicians working in Africa, and give the class a treat. */**/***

26 An African board game An ancient board game called Mancala is played around Africa. It has different names in different countries, for example, it's Owari in Ghana. (It is played on other continents too.) Your task is to find out about Mancala, design and make a Mancala board, find the beans or stones to use, learn the rules, and get playing! */**/***

Population distribution in Africa

27 Work it out The map on page 110 of the students' book is fairly simplified, with the deepest shade representing any number over 100 people per square kilometre. Draw up a table with four columns and these headings: *Country, Population, Area, Population density*. Choose say six countries from the map. List their names in the first column, in order of what you *think* is their population density. Fill in their populations in the second column, using the data on page 110. Look up their areas on the internet, and fill In the third column. Then calculate their population densities, and write these in the last column. Does your table give a better picture of population density than the map? Did you put the countries in the correct order? If yes, give yourself a gold star. **/***

Africa's physical features

28 Google Maps Open Google Maps, and tour around Africa. Try it with labels and photos off, and on. Follow the Nile on its journey. Look at the Nile Delta. Can you find the Suez Canal? The Strait of Gibraltar? Sinai? Explore other features named on the map on page 112 of the students' book. Can you see any settlements in the Sahara? */**/***

29 Choose a physical feature From the map on page 112 of the students' book, pick the physical feature you'd most like to visit. Write a set of geographical questions about it. Then find the answers. And next, find a really good way to present them (perhaps a strip cartoon, an annotated map and photos, a movie, a web page). */**/***

Africa's biomes

30 Rainforest on Google Maps Using the map on page 114 of the students' book to guide you, explore Africa's rainforest biome on Google Maps. Where does most of it seem to have been destroyed? Where is most left? */**/***

31 Other biomes on Google Maps Repeat the above for the other biomes, for example, desert. Look for signs of habitation. */**/***

32 Off on safari You want to see some of Africa's wildlife. Choose a safari park in East Africa. Which one? Plan a trip. Which airport will you fly from? Which forms of travel will you use? Which animals will you see? Write an itinerary, starting from your home. **/***

33 Mountain gorillas There are fewer than 900 of these animals left in the world. Why? Plan a visit to a place where you can see them. */**/***

34 Sum it all up Get a large sheet of sugar paper and do a mind map or spider diagram for all you have learned about Africa. */**/***

35 Africa mastermind In a team, make up quiz questions about Africa, based on what you have covered in class. Challenge the rest of the class against the clock. 1 point to the class for each correct answer, 1 point to the team for each incorrect one. */**/***

7 | In the Horn of Africa

About this chapter

Addressing the KS3 Programme of Study

◆ Students should be taught to understand geographical similarities, differences, and links between places through the study of the human and physical geography of a region in Africa.

About the content

◆ The Horn of Africa is our chosen region because:

- It is a manageable size to study, and in a distinctive location on the map of Africa.
- Its four countries share many characteristics, as well as a long history.
- It has physical features, and livelihoods, that students will find interesting and exotic.
- Its countries are often in the news.

The big picture

These are the key ideas behind this chapter.

◆ The Horn of Africa counts as a geographical region: a large area with a shared history, and several characteristics in common.

◆ It is made up of four countries: Ethiopia, Somalia, Eritrea, and Djibouti. They range in population from small (Djibouti) to the second largest in Africa (Ethiopia).

◆ The region is dominated by the Ethiopian Highlands, but has a range of other interesting

◆ physical features.

◆ Much of it is hot and dry – but it is cooler and wetter up the Ethiopian Highlands.

◆ Most people depend on farming, and the climate dictates what they farm. For example, coffee needs warmth and rain. Nomads have adapted to little rain.

◆ There are other ways to earn a living from the land and sea, such as salt mining, and fishing.

◆ Overall, it is a poor region – but it is developing quite fast.

◆ Djibouti relies on its location for an income.

A students' version of this big picture is given in the *geog.1* students' book opener for Chapter 7, and is the basis of the interactive self-assessment form on *geog.1 Kerboodle*.

The chapter outline

Use this, and their chapter opener, to give students a mental roadmap for the chapter.

7   The Horn of Africa The chapter opener in the students' book is an important part of the chapter; see page 11 for notes about using chapter openers

7.1   Meet the Horn of Africa Where it is in Africa, and the countries that comprise it

7.2   The Horn of Africa: physical features A map of its main physical features, and photos

7.3   The Horn of Africa: climate Compare maps of temperature and rainfall with maps showing population density, and types of farming

7.4   Coffee farming in Ethiopia From the life of a coffee farmer, to Fair Trade coffee

7.5   Life as a nomad How nomads have adapted to the dry climate

7.6   Working as a salt miner Salt mining in the Danakil Depression – and how part of East Africa will become an island one day

7.7   Life on the coast A long coastline – and the profitable business of piracy

7.8   In the city: Addis Ababa Ethiopia's capital, and the main city in the Horn of Africa

7.9   Djibouti: a great location A strategic location at the entrance to the Red Sea

7.10 How is the Horn of Africa doing? Data to explore, including three development indicators

Objectives and outcomes for this chapter

Objectives	Unit	Outcomes
Most students will understand:		Most students will be able to:
• what and where the Horn of Africa is	7.1, 7.7, 7.9	• point to the Horn of Africa on a map; name its four countries and their capitals; name the sea, gulf, and ocean that border it; draw a rough sketch map with all of the above shown and labelled
• that in geography, a region is a large area that shares some common characteristics	7.1	• give at least two reasons why the Horn of Africa counts as a *region*
• that Ethiopia dominates the Horn of Africa in terms of area and population	7.1, 7.10	• list the four countries in order of size and population; say which has a population larger than the UK
• that the Horn of Africa has a variety of physical features	7.2	• name the main physical features, including the Blue Nile and at least one other river; mark them on a sketch map
• that much of the Horn of Africa is hot and dry	7.3	• describe the patterns of temperature and rainfall; say that up in the Ethiopian Highlands it is cooler and wetter
• that overall, the Horn of Africa is a poor region	7.10	• explain what *GDP per person*, and *life expectancy*, mean; say that both are low in the Horn of Africa, relative to the UK
• that most people in the Horn of Africa depend on farming – and farming depends on climate	7.3, 7.4, 7.5	• say that most people depend on farming for a living; describe the pattern of farming, and how it relates to climate; give at least three facts each about coffee farming, and about life as a nomad
• that physical features offer other ways to earn a living	7.6, 7.7	• give at least three facts about salt mining in the Danakil Depression; give at least three facts about life on the coast
• that Addis Ababa is the largest city in the Horn of Africa	7.8	• name Addis Ababa as the capital city of Ethiopia; give six other facts about it
• that Djibouti relies on its location	7.9	• explain how Djibouti benefits from its location; give at least three other facts about Djibouti

These tie in with the outcomes for each unit, in this teacher's handbook, and with 'Your goals for this chapter', in *geog.1* students' book.

Opportunities for assessment

See the formal assessment materials for this chapter on *geog.1 Kerboodle: Lessons, Resources, and Assessments*. They include an extended assessment task, an exam-style question, end-of-lesson assessments, and a self-assessment form. See also the notes on pages 14–15 of this book.

Getting ready for this chapter

geog.1 Kerboodle contains plans and presentations for each unit, including interactive activities, animations, and worksheets.

About 'Your chapter starter'

The photo on page 116 of the students' book shows a woman leading two camels laden with containers of drinking water. She is on her way back from a well, in the Ogaden region of Ethiopia. (See the map on page 120 of the students' book.) She could be a nomad. Note the flat landscape and the low scrubby bushes. This area has no more than 200 mm of rain a year, across two rainy seasons. When the rains fail, even the wells may dry up.

Meet the Horn of Africa

help at a glance

About this unit

This unit introduces the Horn of Africa, and explores its characteristics as a region.

Key points

- The Horn of Africa lies in East Africa, in the tropics.
- It has four countries: Djibouti, Eritrea, Ethiopia, and Somalia.
- It counts as a region because the four countries have much in common, including large areas of semi-desert, and shared history and ethnicity.
- The region is poor overall, and has suffered from much conflict.
- Ethiopia is the only country of the four to be landlocked.

Key vocabulary

Horn of Africa, Greater Horn of Africa, region, Equator, tropics, semi-desert

Skills practised in 'Your turn'

- Geography skills: q1, interpret a map; q4, q5, interpret photos; q6, draw a sketch map
- Numeracy skills: q1–q3, analyse data, and complete a table
- Literacy skills: q4, find words and phrases to describe; q5, describe people's lives
- Thinking skills: q1, logical thinking to allocate data; q5, deduce from a photo

Unit outcomes

By the end of this unit most students should be able to:

- explain the terms given in 'Key vocabulary' above
- say where in Africa the Horn of Africa is, and why it has that name, and point to it on a map
- name the four countries that make up the Horn of Africa, and their capitals
- give at least two reasons why the Horn of Africa counts as a region

Ideas for a starter

1   With books closed, show students an outline map of Africa. Say you are going to study a part of Africa that's shaped like a rhino's horn. Can anyone spot it on the map?

2   With books closed, say: You are going to study a region that includes one of Africa's areas of high land. Guess which one!

3   Show a selection of images from the Horn of Africa, chosen to capture students' interest. Ask for comments. But do not give too much away at this stage!

Ideas for plenaries

Plan plenaries for strategic points throughout the lesson, as well as at the end.

Mid-lesson

1   Before doing any questions: ask students to turn to the world map on pages 140–141 of the students' book. Find the Horn of Africa. Where is it relative to the tropics? Where is it relative to the Equator?

2   Before question 1, say: Look at the map on page 118 of the students' book. Tell me the countries in order of size, from largest to smallest.

3   After question 1, ask a set of questions to firmly establish that Ethiopia is the dominant country in the Horn of Africa in terms of area and population. For example: Compare Ethiopia and Djibouti. About how many times bigger is Ethiopia by area? By population?

(Calculator!) Compare Ethiopia with the other two countries in the same way.

4   After question 5, discuss photo C further. Say: Imagine you are one of these children. Is this hard work? Why are you doing it, rather than a parent? What would happen if you didn't do it? What else do you do to help at home? Do you go to school?

End-of-lesson

5   Are you looking forward to learning more about the Horn of Africa? Why? / Why not?

6   With books closed: Describe the position of the Horn of Africa on the continent of Africa, using as many geographical terms as you can.

7   Who can name the four countries of the Horn of Africa – and their capitals? Who can give the countries in order of size?

Further class and homework opportunities

Suggestions 1–5 on page 164 of this book

geog.1 workbook, page 61

geog.1 Kerboodle: see lesson presentation, worksheets, and end-of-lesson assessment

Answers to 'Your turn'

1

The countries in the Horn of Africa			
Country	Capital	Area (sq km)	Population (millions)
Ethiopia	Addis Ababa	1 127 130	85 237 000
Somalia	Mogadishu	637 660	9 832 000
Eritrea	Asmara	117 600	5 880 000
Djibouti	Djibouti	23 000	906 000

2   Ethiopia

3   Eritrea, Djibouti

4   a   Expect words and phrases like: mountainous, hilly, steep slopes, peaks, valleys, big rock, green, grassy, small trees, stretching into the distance.

b   Expect words and phrases like: dry ground, bumpy ground, stony ground, no grass, few trees, hilly.

5   Students might note / deduce: no running water in homes; no sign of electricity; donkeys as transport; the conical hut may be a home; land does not show signs of organised farming; young girls are expected to fetch water. Do these girls go to school? Where are the boys?

For your information: this photo was taken in Eritrea. The label on the metal container indicates that it once held fortified vegetable oil – fortified with vitamin A, which is needed for growth and development, and good vision. It appears to have been supplied by the USA, which suggests that the local people may depend on food aid to at least some extent.

6   This activity could round off the lesson.

About this unit

This unit presents a map showing the main physical features of the Horn of Africa, and photos of some of them.

Key points

- The Horn of Africa has an exciting range of physical features.
- It is dominated by the Ethiopian Highlands, the largest area of high land in Africa. These are divided by the Rift Valley, which contains a string of lakes.
- The rivers rise in the Ethiopian Highlands. The Blue Nile is the most famous. It flows out of Ethiopia and eventually joins the White Nile, to form the Nile.
- The Afar Triangle is a triangle of low land bordering the Red Sea that shows signs of tectonic activity: earthquakes and volcanic eruptions. In fact tectonic plates are pulling apart here. The low land and Rift Valley will drop further, and eventually flood with ocean water. Ten million years from now, much of East Africa will be an island. (See the image on page 129 of the students' books.)
- Lake Assal, in the Afar Triangle, is the lowest point in Africa.
- The Ogaden is a plateau where nomads graze animals.
- Somalia has the longest coastline in Africa.

Key vocabulary

physical features, highlands, volcano, earthquake, plateau, nomads, grazing

Skills practised in 'Your turn'

- Geography skills: q1–q4, q6, interpret a map; q8, interpret photos; q9, draw a sketch map
- Literacy skills: q1, q7, define
- Thinking skills: q5, identify interesting facts; q8, explain choice

Unit outcomes

By the end of this unit most students should be able to:

- explain the terms given in 'Key vocabulary' above
- interpret a map of the physical features of the Horn of Africa
- name and describe the main physical features of the Horn of Africa, including the Ethiopian Highlands and their highest peak, the Blue Nile and at least one other river, the Afar Triangle and Danakil Depression, Lake Assal, and the Dallol and Erta Ale volcanoes
- name the sea, gulf, and ocean that border the region

Ideas for a starter

1   Say: We are going to study physical features of the Horn of Africa. What are *physical features*? Name some. You can write a list on the board.

2   Display photographs of physical features in the Horn of Africa, showing the diversity of landscapes, and some of the spectacular and unusual geographical features. For example Dallol, and Lake Assal with its 'beaches' of salt.

3   With books closed, say: You will find all of these in the Horn of Africa. Who can unjumble the words?

   dnghihals   skeal   ulapeta   sclavoen   svirer   sebache   qhareetuks

   Give students just a few minutes. They can watch out for unsolved ones during the lesson.

Ideas for plenaries

Plan plenaries for strategic points throughout the lesson, as well as at the end.

Mid-lesson

1   Look back at and discuss the photo of the Ethiopian Highlands on page 118 of the students' book.

2   Ask for comments about the kinds of physical features shown in the photos on pages 120–121 of the students' book. Which have vegetation? Which are you unlikely to find in the UK? Which are the most unusual? Which might be exciting to visit? Which might be dangerous?

3   Imagine you are one of the people herding goats in the Ogaden. What will you say about your life?

End-of-lesson

4   Make up answers like those below, with a bit of a twist. What is the question?

    a   Because it is shaped like a triangle

    b   Lake Assal

    c   Because it is a mountainous area

    d   Pasture

    e   A lava lake

    f   Sulfuric acid

5   The class stands up. Each student states one fact about the Horn of Africa, learned from the last two units, then sits down. But if the fact is incorrect, or a repetition of what someone else said, he or she must stand up again. How quickly can everyone be sitting?

6   Give the class 5 minutes to make up an acrostic about the Horn of Africa, based on the term *ETHIOPIAN HIGHLANDS*. Each capital letter can take up any position in a sentence, phrase or term.

Further class and homework opportunities

Suggestions 6–13 on page 164 of this book

geog.1 workbook, page 62

geog.1 Kerboodle: see lesson presentation, worksheets, and end-of-lesson assessment

Answers to 'Your turn'

1   **a**   Ethiopia   **b**   A flattish raised area of land

2   Highest: Ras Dashen; lowest, Lake Assal

3   Lake Tana

4   **a**   River Awash

    b   Their common feature is that they rise in the Ethiopian Highlands. Of the rivers shown, two eventually flow north west, out of Ethiopia, and three south east; eventually all three become part of the River Jubba. The Omo and Awash are different: both flow into lakes. (These lakes do not spill over because water evaporates, and seeps out through the bottom of the lake.)

5   Answers will vary.

6   **a**   Eritrea   **b**   Somalia

7   A large area of ocean that is partly enclosed by land

8   Answers will vary.

9   You could suggest that students try the sketch map without rivers first, and later add the Blue Nile and at least one other river.

The Horn of Africa: climate

help at a glance

About this unit

This unit presents maps of temperature and rainfall in the Horn of Africa; and maps of population density and farming to compare with them.

Key points

◆ The Horn of Africa lies within the tropics, with the Equator passing through southern Somalia. So the region is warm to hot all year.

◆ However, as you go up the Ethiopian Highlands, the climate cools.

◆ There is wide variation in rainfall, with most falling in the Ethiopian Highlands.

◆ The rest of the Horn is dry to very dry: it is largely semi-desert, with sparse vegetation. The rains here frequently fail, leading to drought.

◆ Most people in the Horn of Africa depend on farming for a living.

◆ In the dry areas, people usually raise animals for a living, and travel with them to find grazing. They are nomads.

◆ In the wetter areas, people grow crops and raise animals.

◆ Overall, population density is lower in the drier areas, where it is hard to grow crops.

Key vocabulary

climate, temperature, annual rainfall, population density, nomad

Skills practised in 'Your turn'

◆ Geography skills: q1–q4, q10, interpret maps; q6–q8, interpret and compare maps, looking for similar patterns

◆ Literacy skills: q5, define

◆ Thinking skills: q2, q6–q10, explain

Unit outcomes

By the end of this unit most students should be able to:

◆ explain the terms given in 'Key vocabulary' above

◆ describe the patterns of temperature and rainfall

◆ say that overall, much of the region is hot and dry, and frequently suffers drought

◆ say that it is both cooler and wetter in the Ethiopian Highlands

◆ say that most people depend on farming for a living

◆ describe the pattern of farming, and how it relates to climate

◆ describe the pattern of population density, and how it relates to climate

Ideas for a starter

1 With books closed, write the heading *Climate* on the board. Then say: Who can tell me what *climate* means? Write up any phrases.

2 With books closed, say: The word *climate* means what the weather in a place is *usually* like, at different times of year. What do you think the climate is like, in the Horn of Africa? Write phrases on the board. Each time, ask: Why do you think that?

3 With books closed, explain what the word *climate* means. Then say: Get ready to look at some images, with clues about the climate of the Horn of Africa. Start with a map of Africa, with the Equator and tropics marked in. Then show other images, for example, of lush vegetation, and rivers, and parched semi-desert. Ask what students have deduced about the climate. Write phrases on the board. You can come back to these later.

Ideas for plenaries

Plan plenaries for strategic points throughout the lesson, as well as at the end.

Mid-lesson

1 Do any or all of the questions in 'Your turn' as plenaries.

2 Spend some time on each map on the spread, to make sure students understand them. Then look back at the photo on page 116 of the students' book. Where would you place it on the temperature map? Or the rainfall map? On the farming map?

3 Discuss map B on page 122 of the students' book. Why does Ethiopia have more rainfall than the other countries? Look back at the map on page 120. Any clues?

4 Look at the darkest areas on map C (population density) on page 122 of the students' book. Who can be first to tell me what they correspond to? The map on page 118 has clues. (Capital cities.)

End-of-lesson

5 Ask: Did you enjoy comparing the maps in this unit, looking for patterns? Did you find it hard? Easy? Why? Do you think maps can tell you a lot?

6 Say: Let's try and sum up the climate of the Horn of Africa in three clear and correct sentences.

7 Ask: Do you agree that farmers in the Horn of Africa are influenced by the climate? Do you think that might be true of other regions too? Can you think of examples?

8 Why do we bother to learn about climate?

Further class and homework opportunities

Suggestions 14–18 on page 164 of this book

geog.1 workbook, page 63

geog.1 Kerboodle: see lesson presentation, worksheets, and end-of-lesson assessment

Answers to 'Your turn'

1 Because it all lies within the tropics, and the Equator passes through it.

2 a It shows the average temperature in July, in the Horn of Africa.

   b W

   c W is in the Ethiopian Highlands. The higher you go, the lower the temperature.

3 a It shows annual rainfall in the Horn of Africa.

   b i 1000–2000 mm ii 0–200 mm

   c Y

4 Statement A is true.

5 The average number of people living in a place, per square kilometre.

6 a In general, the cooler places (which are in the Ethiopian Highlands) appear to be more densely populated.

   b An average temperature of 30–35°C is very hot. (It is the average of day and night temperatures.) People will find it more comfortable to live in cooler areas. If the hotter areas also have little or no rainfall (as is the case here), crops won't grow.

7 Again, the areas with more rain (which are mainly in the Ethiopian highlands) appear to have a higher population density. In the areas with low rainfall, it will be difficult or impossible to grow crops. In areas of higher rainfall (where it is also warm) crops will grow well, and people will be better able to feed themselves and grow food for sale.

8 There is quite a good correlation between the two maps. People in the dry areas rear animals, and travel with them to find vegetation: they are nomads. People in the areas with more rainfall grow crops. They can also rear animals, without the need to be nomadic. Coffee obviously needs warmth and quite a lot of rain.

9 a In the drier areas, rainfall is erratic. When the rains fail, rivers may dry up, and the water level in wells falls. Vegetation dies back, and crops shrivel. Neither animals nor people have enough food or water. Both die.

   b The bodies of young children, and their immune systems, are still developing. So they are more vulnerable than adults.

10 These strips lie along rivers. Presumably the farmers use river water for irrigation.

Coffee farming in Ethiopia

About this unit

This unit is about coffee farming in Ethiopia, and the life of the coffee farmer.

Key points

◆ Coffee is Ethiopia's top export; around 15 million Ethiopians depend on it, directly or indirectly, for a living.

◆ Most of the coffee is grown on small family farms; many of the farmers belong to co-operatives, which sell the coffee on their behalf.

◆ The price of coffee beans fluctuates on the world market, in response to changes in supply and demand.

◆ In years of oversupply, the farmers may earn very little for a coffee crop: barely enough to survive.

◆ More coffee co-ops in Ethiopia are joining the Fair Trade movement, through which they can earn a fairer price, plus some extra to help their communities.

Key vocabulary

co-operative, export, profit, Fair Trade

Skills practised in 'Your turn'

◆ Geography skills: q1, analyse maps

◆ Literacy skills: q5, design an advert

◆ Thinking skills: q2, list people in the coffee supply chain; q3, explain, and predict; q4, decide, and give reasons

Unit outcomes

By the end of this unit most students should be able to:

◆ explain the terms given in 'Key vocabulary' above

◆ say that coffee is Ethiopia's top export

◆ say that coffee beans are extracted from cherries that grow on trees

◆ explain why the price of coffee beans rises and falls from year to year

◆ say that most of Ethiopia's coffee farmers are poor

◆ explain what Fair Trade coffee is

Ideas for a starter

1 With books closed: show / pass around some jars and packets of coffee. Include roasted coffee beans. Ask: How much can you tell me about coffee? Is it from a fruit? A leaf? A vegetable? From herbs? Is it grown in the UK? Write words and phrases on the board, perhaps under different headings. You can come back to them later.

2 Ask: Hands up who has drunk coffee? What did you think of it? Why do so many people like it? What coffee bars are there around here?

3 With books closed, and without comment, show images of coffee, starting with growers (preferably in Ethiopia) and working along the supply chain to the customer in a coffee bar. Then ask: What is the link between those images?

Ideas for plenaries

Plan plenaries for strategic points throughout the lesson, as well as at the end.

Mid-lesson

1 Look at the first photo on page 124 of the students' book. Describe what you see. What is Abel's house like? Do you think he has electricity? Running water?

2 Ask a student to read out Abel's story. Other students can sit with books closed.

3 Display a graph from the internet showing how the price of coffee fluctuates. At what point on the graph might farmers be happy? At what point might they be unhappy?

4 Ask: About how much is a cup of coffee in a café? Abel earned £690 one year. How many cups of coffee could he buy?

End-of-lesson

5 Pass around some packets / jars of Fair Trade coffee. Do you think the Fair Trade movement is a good idea? Why? / Why not? Have you seen any other Fair Trade goods on sale?

6 Imagine you are a coffee drinker. You buy Ethiopian coffee every week. Do you think you have any effect on Abel's life? Why? / Why not?

7 Ask students to write *COFFEE FARMING* down a page. They use this as the base for an acrostic, made up of sentences about coffee farming in Ethiopia. One condition: they must include a sentence about the kind of climate coffee needs.

Further class and homework opportunities

Suggestions 19–26 on pages 164–165 of this book

geog.1 workbook, page 64

geog.1 Kerboodle: see lesson presentation, worksheets, and end-of-lesson assessment

Answers to 'Your turn'

1 Statement B is true.

2 Students could mention: coffee farmer; people who extract the beans; people who check them for quality; people who buy them from the coffee co-op to export them; packers; truck drivers; port workers; shippers; importing company, which processes the coffee; more truck drivers; supermarket staff.

3 a The more coffee that's grown around the world, the lower the price, as a general rule. Also the four big buyers (Sarah Lee, Procter and Gamble, Kraft, and Nestlé) have a big influence on the price, and can push it down since they buy in such bulk. Their main interest is in profits, not farmers' livelihoods. (But note that they have all been taking some steps towards treating the coffee farmers more fairly.)

b Because the farmers don't know how much money they will get, they can't plan for the future. For example, they don't know whether or not they will be able to afford new coffee plants, or fertiliser; they don't know if they will be able to afford to send their children to school, or pay for basic healthcare.

4 If the farmers grew food instead of coffee, it could mean more and cheaper food for local people, which would be good. (Ethiopia currently imports much of its food.) But Ethiopia would then lose the money it earns from exporting coffee. So it would have less to spend on education, healthcare, and other important things. (In addition, Ethiopians drink a lot of coffee. If farmers stopped growing it, the country might have to import some!)

5 This could be for homework.

Life as a nomad

help at a glance

About this unit

This unit explores the way of life of the nomads in the Horn of Africa.

Key points

◆ Nomads live in the drier parts of the Horn of Africa, where it is difficult to grow crops.

◆ They respond to the climate by rearing animals (goats, sheep, camels, and sometimes cattle) and travelling with them to find grazing (vegetation to eat).

◆ Where and when there is grazing depends in turn on the rainfall patterns.

◆ In their travels, they may cross borders, for example, from Somalia into Ethiopia or Kenya.

◆ There are at least 10 million nomads in the Horn of Africa.

◆ The nomadic lifestyle in effect turns poor land into meat and milk.

◆ The nomads sell animals and milk in markets, to earn money to buy cereals such as maize.

◆ The animals may be bought by traders, for export. The Horn countries export hundreds of thousands of pounds' worth of animals a year.

◆ Nomadic life is hard, and made more difficult by unreliable rains, civil wars and other conflicts, and competition for grazing.

Key vocabulary

nomad, grazing, vegetation, export

Skills practised in 'Your turn'

◆ Geography skills: q2, q3, interpret photos

◆ Literacy skills: q2, q6, write lists

◆ Thinking skills: q1, q3–q5, explain; q2, deduce; q6, make suggestions; q7, make predictions

Unit outcomes

By the end of this unit most students should be able to:

◆ explain the terms given in 'Key vocabulary' above

◆ explain why people become nomads

◆ describe the life of a nomad

◆ say that nomads produce milk and meat from natural vegetation and poor soil

◆ list three factors that make the nomadic life more difficult, in the Horn of Africa

◆ explain the importance of nomads to the Horn of Africa

Ideas for a starter

1 Ask: Have you ever slept in a tent and cooked on a camp fire? What if you had to do it year after year? What problems might you face?

2 Show photos of nomads. For example: reindeer herders in the Arctic, the Tuareg of North Africa, the nomads of Mongolia. Try to include their tents. What do these people have in common? Why do they move? Help the class to develop a definition of nomadism. Say there are millions of nomads around the world (perhaps 30–40 million).

3 Ten thousand years ago, there were perhaps only a few hundred people living in the UK. They did not stay in one place. They moved around: they were nomads. Why? (They were hunter gatherers, like everyone before farming began.)

Ideas for plenaries

Plan plenaries for strategic points throughout the lesson, as well as at the end.

Mid-lesson

1 Ask a student or students to read aloud 'Safiyo's day'. Then discuss it. Use 'Your turn' questions 1 and 2 as plenaries.

2 Discuss each photo in the unit in turn. How much can you observe? For example, what is Safiyo's home made of? What kinds of animals can you see at the well? What can you say about the village?

3 Conflict in a country – for example, civil war in Somalia – makes the lives of nomads more difficult. Why?

End-of-lesson

4 To survive, nomads must be very resourceful! Do you think you'd have the skills to survive in such difficult conditions? Who would be able to teach you?

5 Ask students to imagine they are part of a nomadic family in the Horn of Africa. Ask: Which do you think are your family's most valuable possessions? Why?

6 Use starter 2 as a plenary.

7 Would it be possible to live like a nomad in the UK? Why / Why not? Can you think of people who do? (There are around 300 000 Gypsies, Roma, and Travellers, in the UK. Some still have a nomadic lifestyle, but a range of ways of making a living.)

Further class and homework opportunities

Suggestions 27–29 on page 165 of this book

geog.1 workbook, page 65

geog.1 Kerboodle: see lesson presentation, worksheets, and end-of-lesson assessment

Answers to 'Your turn'

1 Because they live in semi-desert areas where it's too dry, and the ground too poor, to grow crops; so rearing animals offers a livelihood. But their animals quickly eat up the vegetation in an area. So they must travel with them to find more grazing – and that means following the rains. (Vegetation flourishes in rainy seasons.)

2 Students might mention: no running water, no toilets, no electricity, no fridge to keep things fresh, small huts, rain leaking into the huts in wet weather, long distances to travel, no doctors nearby, continual worry about the rains, and about money to buy maize, little or no education for children.

3 For water, students might mention: long distances to walk to wells; hard work drawing water from wells (and the longer it has been since rain, the lower the water level in the well); and water is heavy to carry. For firewood: there are not many bushes; you have to go further and further each day; you must avoid taking branches with leaves that camels and goats can eat.

4 Their animals are the nomads' wealth. They can drink their milk, eat their meat, and sell them and their skins. They can buy other food with the money. During drought, vegetation shrivels up. Eventually there will be nothing for the animals to eat, so they die. At the same time, water levels in wells fall. Wells may even dry up. So the nomads do not have enough to drink, and nothing to sell in exchange for food. They too may die, from starvation.

5 They rear animals on poor land that's not much use for anything else. Many of the animals are exported, which earns money for the Horn countries. Some, or their milk or meat, are sold locally. That benefits the Horn countries too.

6 Suggestions: reading and writing, counting (say to 1000), arithmetic for simple calculations, money / currency, units for weighing and measuring things, the main official language of their country, the geography of their country, simple healthcare and nutrition for themselves (for example, making sure water is safe to drink); healthcare for their animals.

7 They'd have to move into areas with fertile land and more rain, to grow crops, or move to towns and cities. It might be hard to find land, or to find work in towns and cities, since there is high unemployment. Their presence might be resented. They might find it hard to settle down. Their culture would disappear. Meanwhile, the number of animals being raised would fall dramatically, affecting both local food supplies, and exports. However, for individual nomads, life might be a lot better. There would be school for the children, and perhaps doctors and clinics. There is likely to be water, from standpipes.

Working as a salt miner

About this unit

This unit explores salt mining in Ethiopia, and what life is like for a salt miner.

Key points

◆ The Danakil Depression is a low, flat, area in the Afar Triangle, about 100 m below sea level. It is extremely hot and dry.

◆ Once it was flooded with seawater, which was then trapped; the water evaporated, leaving thick beds of salt.

◆ At present, salt is mined from the salt beds by hand, using traditional methods.

◆ In the future, machinery may mine the salt, and threaten livelihoods.

◆ Millions of years from now, the Danakil Depression will be under water again. That's because tectonic plates are moving apart, down East Africa. The Afar Triangle and Rift Valley are dropping lower. Eventually ocean water will flood in, cutting off a large chunk of East Africa as an island.

Key vocabulary

salt beds, evaporate, salt caravan, tax

Skills practised in 'Your turn'

◆ Geography skills: q4, interpret a photo; q6, interpret a map

◆ Literacy skills: q2, write with empathy; q3, write a list; q4, write to describe

◆ Thinking skills: q3, come up with uses; q5, predict consequences; q6, explain

Unit outcomes

By the end of this unit most students should be able to:

◆ explain the terms given in 'Key vocabulary' above

◆ say where the Danakil Depression is

◆ say where the salt in the Danakil Depression came from

◆ give at least three facts about salt mining in the Danakil Depression

◆ explain why a chunk of East Africa, including most of the Horn of Africa, will eventually become an island

Ideas for a starter

1 Bring in some salt: fine salt, and sea crystals. Ask: What is salt? Where does it come from? Is any found in the UK? (Most of the salt used in the UK is extracted from under the ground in County Antrim, Cleveland, and Cheshire. It is mined as rock salt, or dissolved underground and pumped out as brine.)

2 Say: Salt was once used as money, in Ethiopia. Why is salt so valuable? Then, with books still closed, do 'Your turn' question 3 and write suggestions on the board.

3 Show stunning images of salt mining in the Horn of Africa, including at the Danakil Depression, and Lake Assal in Djibouti. (Try the *National Geographic* site among others.) Add images of salt mining in the UK for contrast.

Ideas for plenaries

Plan plenaries for strategic points throughout the lesson, as well as at the end.

Mid-lesson

1   Ask a student, or students, to read 'Dejen's day' aloud. Then discuss this work as a way to earn a living.

2   Ask: Why do they use camels to carry the salt?

3   Ask: Why are the Afar at Hamed Ela anxious to keep machinery out?

End-of-lesson

4   Which do you think would be more efficient at extracting salt: a machine, or Dejen?

   Is it always better to go for the more efficient option? Why do you think that?

5   Imagine: You are a salt merchant at Mekele. You have plans for making salt mining more efficient, in the Danakil Depression. Tell us your plans. Also list all the problems you expect to face.

6   Show images of salt mining in the UK. Ask: How does the work compare with Dejen's?

7   Ask students to think of a name for the new island to be formed by a chunk of East Africa, about 10 million years from now. Ask: Do you think humans will be around to see it?

Further class and homework opportunities

Suggestions 30–33 on page 165 of this book

geog.1 workbook, page 66

geog.1 Kerboodle: see lesson presentation, worksheets, and end-of-lesson assessment

Answers to 'Your turn'

1   Sea water once flooded this area, became trapped, and then evaporated, leaving the salt behind.

2   You are likely to feel boiling hot within seconds, doing that job. Your skin will feel scorched. Your feet will feel on fire – from the ground below and the Sun above. Sweat will pour into your eyes. The hot dry air will sear your lungs. Your arms and shoulders will ache. You will yearn for a drink of water.

3   Students will probably have difficulty coming up with more than a couple of uses.

   There are hundreds. Below are some likely to apply in Ethiopia.

   • Salt is an essential part of our diet. The sodium in it is essential for many body processes. We would die without it. Our bodies can't make sodium, so we must take it in, in food.

   • It is essential for animals too. They may get some from licking natural mineral deposits in the ground. But often farmers provide an artificial salt lick – a block of rock salt that the animals lick when they need to.

   • As well as being essential for our diet, salt also adds flavour.

   • It is used in preserving foods such as meat and fish, and in tanning animal skins to make leather.

   • It is used in making soap and paper.

   • It is used in dyeing fabrics.

4   The photo shows the salt caravan passing along the canyon of the Saba River. At certain times of year – as here – the river dries to a trickle.

   Students might mention: everything being very brown; steep stony slopes, with few trees; camel after camel plodding past, each laden; a few camel drivers on foot.

5   Possible negative consequences: trucks could bring mining machinery, so Dejen will lose his job; trucks could carry the salt away, so no need for the salt caravans; without the visiting salt caravans, Hamed Ela might close down as a village; there might be ongoing conflict between the mining company and the local Afar.

   Possible positive consequences: Dejen might get a job operating the machinery; the new road could bring opportunities for other jobs, such as guiding tourists, or running a café for the truck drivers; trucks can bring supplies of food and water, and other things; a new road might bring buses or bus-taxis too, so Dejan could go to Berahile or Mekele to find work, and come back at weekends to his village; with a new road, it will be easier for people to go to hospital, or school, or for aid to get to the village.

6   The Horn of Africa will one day become part of a new long thin island because it is part of a big chunk of East Africa that will be cut off from the rest of Africa. In this part of Africa, Earth's crust is being torn apart – and in time, the ocean will flood in. We can tell this is happening from the earthquakes and volcanic activity in the area.

Life on the coast

help at a glance

About this unit

This unit looks at the coast of the Horn of Africa, and the period of piracy.

Key points

◆ The Horn of Africa has a long coastline.

◆ A coastal country has special rights over the sea and sea floor, in its own exclusive economic zone.

◆ The coastal countries of the Horn could earn money from fishing, and tourism.

◆ However, for decades, Eritrea and Somalia neglected their fishing industries, because of conflict – and conflict keeps tourists away.

◆ The ocean off Somalia is busy for shipping, since the shipping route through the Gulf of Aden and Suez Canal is the world's second busiest.

◆ In Somalia, during the civil war that started in 1991, piracy developed as a way to make money. Ships on their way to and from the Gulf of Aden were hijacked, and held to ransom.

◆ By 2013 piracy had almost stopped, mainly because ships carried armed guards, and were often protected by warships.

Key vocabulary

landlocked, exclusive economic zone (EEZ), tourism, conflict, piracy, ransom

Skills practised in 'Your turn'

◆ Geography skills: q1, interpret a map

◆ Literacy skills: q1, write a list; q2, q3, define

◆ Thinking skills: q1, come up with advantages; q3–q6, give reasons

Unit outcomes

By the end of this unit most students should be able to:

◆ explain the terms given in 'Key vocabulary' above

◆ say which countries of the Horn of Africa have coastlines

◆ say how these countries could earn money from their coastlines

◆ explain why the coast of the Horn of Africa does not attract many tourists

◆ tell the story of piracy off Somalia

◆ explain how and why piracy started, and why it had died away by 2013

Ideas for a starter

1   With books closed, ask: Who can sketch the coastline of the Horn of Africa, and name the countries that share it? Who can name the three areas of water? You could ask a student to sketch it on the board. Other students can direct and comment.

2   Who owns the waters around the UK? (Answer: the Crown (Crown Estate) *owns* the territorial sea and sea bed, a belt 22 km wide, measured from the mean low-water mark. It has *rights* in the exclusive economic zone (EEZ), which extends from the mean low-water mark out to 370 km.)

3   Ask: What do you know about pirates? Do you think there are still pirates today?

Ideas for plenaries

Plan plenaries for strategic points throughout the lesson, as well as at the end.

Mid-lesson

1   Look at the map on page 130 of the students' book. Which capital cities are also ports?

2   Eritrea used to be part of Ethiopia. After years of conflict, it gained independence in 1993. Ethiopia badly wanted to keep Eritrea. Why? (Coastline, and ports.)

3   Turn back to the map on page 113 of the students' book. Say: Suppose ships are bringing clothing and other goods from China to the UK. Ask: If it's not safe to sail near Somalia, where would they have to go instead? What are the implications for you? (More expensive goods!)

4   Ask: If there had not been civil war in Somalia … would there still have been pirates? Explain your answer.

5   Discuss the photos and their captions. For example, ask: Have you ever eaten swordfish? Why was such a big ransom paid for the Sirius Star?

End-of-lesson

6   Ask students to tell you the three most interesting things they have learned in today's lesson.

7   Do an acrostic based on *COASTLINE* to sum up today's lesson. The capital letters can take any position in the words, phrases, and sentences that students write.

8   Ask: Is it fair that coastal countries should have an EEZ? Explain.

9   Ask: From all that you've learned so far, what would make you want to visit the Horn of Africa as a tourist? And what would put you off?

Further class and homework opportunities

Suggestions 34–38 on page 165 of this book

geog.1 workbook, page 67

geog.1 Kerboodle: see lesson presentation, worksheets, and end-of-lesson assessment

Answers to 'Your turn'

1 a All except Ethiopia!

   b Coasts offer the opportunity for: fishing, trade, and travel by ship (through ports) with other countries, and leisure activities (swimming, sailing, diving, snorkelling, lazing on beaches) for local people as well as tourists. (And tourism brings in money.) In addition a coastal country has an EEZ, which might have oil or gas. The EEZ could be used for offshore windfarms, or for wave power. Coasts are also useful in times of war, for moving people, and weapons, to other places.

2 a It has no coastline.   b Djibouti

3 a Exclusive economic zone

   b It gives the country exclusive rights for fishing and exploration of the sea floor. Other countries cannot exploit the EEZ without permission.

   c Yes. At almost 7 million square km, it is the fifth largest in the world. It includes not only the EEZ around the UK itself, but also around the UK's overseas territories (including the Falkland

Islands, disputed with Argentina) and Crown Dependencies (Isle of Man and Channel Islands).

4   Mainly because of the armed conflicts over many decades, all around the Horn, including the civil war that started in Somalia in 1991. In addition, countries of the Horn are often in the news because of drought and famine, and more recently, piracy in Somalia. None of this encourages tourism.

5   Because the shipping route from the Gulf of Aden, through the Red Sea and Suez Canal, is extremely busy – the second busiest shipping route in the world, after the Panama Canal

6 a They were angry at foreign fishing boats fishing illegally in their waters.

   b Somalia is poor, and piracy was a way to earn large sums of money quite fast. Also law and order had broken down, so there was nobody to prevent piracy. Businessmen were encouraging it, as an investment. And armed groups were probably using it as a way to get funds.

In the city: Addis Ababa

help at a glance

About this unit

This unit gives a glimpse of life in Addis Ababa – Ethiopia's capital city, and the biggest city in the Horn of Africa.

Key points

- Addis Ababa is Ethiopia's capital city, and the biggest city in the Horn of Africa.
- Its population is around 4.2 million, and growing fast.
- It has a special status in Africa, largely because Ethiopia was never colonised. Many international organisations are based in Addis, including the African Union.
- Over half of the formal housing in Addis is owned by the government. (This dates back to 1974, when the new Marxist regime nationalised land and rental housing in order to help the poor.) But this housing has suffered from years of neglect.
- Over the decades many thousands of informal shacks have also sprung up, as new people arrive in Addis.
- The result is that over 75% of Addis is considered to be slums.
- Now the government is carrying out an ambitious plan to build hundreds of thousands of affordable flats, for people to buy. The aim is to clear the slums away.

Key vocabulary

population, slum, colonise

Skills practised in 'Your turn'

- Geography skills: q1, q3, interpret maps; q2, q6, interpret photos
- Literacy skills: q2, describe features, from photos
- Thinking skills: q4, weigh up pros and cons; q5, predict problems; q6, q7, give reasons

Unit outcomes

By the end of this unit most students should be able to:

- explain the terms given in 'Key vocabulary' above
- name Addis Ababa as the capital of Ethiopia, and say where it is in Ethiopia
- say that slums – areas of run-down housing, and shacks – are a big feature of Addis Ababa
- say that hundreds of thousands of affordable homes are being built, and slums will be cleared away
- give at least four other facts about Addis Abba

Ideas for a starter

1. With books closed: Only two countries in Africa were never colonised. Ask: Can you remember which two? (Answer: Ethiopia and Liberia)

2. With books closed, ask: Which do you think is the biggest city in the Horn of Africa? From what you know about the sizes of the countries, see if you can guess! (You could provide an anagram. For example: aaaabbddsi.)

3. Show a range of photos of Addis Ababa. You could include slums, and the current headquarters of the African Union, opened in 2012. It was built by China, as a gift to Africa. It is the tallest building in Addis.

Ideas for plenaries

Plan plenaries for strategic points throughout the lesson, as well as at the end.

Mid-lesson

1   Study each photo in turn. Ask: What does it tell you about the city?

2   Mebrete is only 14, but he started work when he was 11. Ask: Why do you think he has to work? What could be done to make sure that he does not have to work?

3   Imagine: You are Mebrete. How would you enjoy that job? What are the good and bad things about it?

4   After question 4: Discuss council housing in the UK. Is it similar to the rented housing in Addis? (In 2010, about 17% of the UK population were living in council flats.)

5   Before question 5: Why do you think people would chose to move to Addis Ababa? Then do 'Your turn' question 5 as a plenary.

End-of-lesson

6   Compare Addis Ababa and London. Ask: What do they have in common? What is different? List some problems and advantages for each city.

7   Some of the people who have moved to the new high rise flats are not happy. They do not have room in their kitchens for making big family meals, including *injera* (flat bread, like very large pancakes). And, having lived at ground level, living high up is a challenge. Ask: What makes a house a home? Is it just about the building, or is it more?

8   The organisation called the African Union is based in Addis. It wants to promote peace and improve people's lives, in Africa. Ask: From what you have learned about the continent and people of Africa so far, what suggestions do you have for them?

Further class and homework opportunities

Suggestions 39–41 on page 165 of this book

geog.1 workbook, page 68

geog.1 Kerboodle: see lesson presentation, worksheets, and end-of-lesson assessment

Answers to 'Your turn'

1   It is almost in the centre of Ethiopia (slightly west of centre). It is up in the Ethiopian Highlands.

2   Students might comment on: the tall buildings downtown, the hills in the background, quite a lot of greenery, the wide roads in this part, not much traffic when this photo was taken, the building with the flags on the left. Look at the area of low housing on the right of the photo, in front of the tall buildings. That is a slum.

3   Students may have difficulty in judging where Addis Ababa is, on maps A and B.

Point out the area of higher population density in the middle of Ethiopia on map C. That is Addis. From here they should be able to deduce that Addis has quite a cool climate (15–20 °C in July), with quite a lot of rain (1000–2000 mm). In fact the average daily temperature in July is 15.9 °C, and the average annual rainfall is 1165 mm; and on average, it rains on 132 days of the year.

4   Point out that it would be like having lots and lots of low-rent council flats. (In 2010, about 17% of the UK population were living in council flats.)

Pros: people on low wages could afford the rent. You would not be at the mercy of private landlords. With low rents, people would have more money to spend on other things. There'd be less pressure to buy a place. It would be up to the government to make sure that the buildings were kept in good repair.

Cons: the government would not get much income from low-rent flats, so might not spend much on looking after them. Lots of people would end up living in similar places, which could be boring. We like variety. There would be less of a role for private companies in supplying homes. This would have a negative effect on the economy.

5   That many people arriving every year will put huge pressure on the city. People will need somewhere to live. They might have to build their own shacks. They will need water, and food. They will want work – and employment is already high in Addis. There will be more sewage and rubbish to dispose of. There will be more people needing doctors, and hospitals. There will be more children, who need schooling.

6   If they can't find anywhere to live, or can't afford even the low rents in the government housing, people may have no option but to find a space and build a shack.

7   Poor accommodation is linked to poor health, and can lead to social unrest. Addis has big issues of water supply and sewage disposal, which it is beginning to tackle through the new flats. The flat-building programme has led to many people acquiring building skills, and many new jobs. As headquarters of the African Union, Addis needs to set an example as a modern African city.

7.9　Djibouti: a great location

help at a glance

About this unit

This unit looks at Djibouti, the smallest country in the Horn of Africa, which relies on its strategic location.

Key points

- Djibouti is a small country: area 23 000 sq km, population around 906 000.
  So it is only about 2000 sq km larger than Wales, and has fewer people than Birmingham.
- 70% of its population live in the capital, also called Djibouti.
- In general, it is hot, dry, and semi-desert.
- It earns money through its port, at the entrance to the Red Sea, on the world's second busiest shipping route. It is the main port for Ethiopia.
- Djibouti is also a strategic base for American and French forces fighting terrorism in North Africa, and warships patrolling off Somalia, to prevent piracy.
- Because it is semi-desert, with little fertile land, most food has to be imported.
- Although it is considered a middle income African country by the World Bank, it has a high percentage of people living in poverty, and high unemployment. 40% of people live on less than $2 a day.
- The government is trying to tackle these challenges by expanding its port, welcoming tourists, and inviting foreign companies in, including foreign banks.

Key vocabulary

location, port, military base, unemployment, tourism

Skills practised in 'Your turn'

- Geography skills: q2, draw a sketch map, to explain the importance of a location
- Literacy skills: q1, unjumble words and complete sentences; q3, q5, write lists; q6, design an advert
- Thinking skills: q2, make decisions; q4, explain; q5, come up with examples

Unit outcomes

By the end of this unit most students should be able to:

- explain the terms given in 'Key vocabulary' above
- describe Djibouti's location in the Gulf of Aden, at the entrance to the Red Sea
- say how Djibouti benefits from this location
- give at least three other facts about Djibouti

Ideas for a starter

1. Recap, with books closed: Who can name the sea that connects the Indian Ocean to the Mediterranean Sea? What is at each end of it? Many ships pass along it. Why?
2. Recap, with books closed: What can you tell me about Djibouti? Where exactly is it?
   It's a long way from France, but French is one of its official languages. What does that tell you? (The other official language is Arabic.)
3. Show a set of images of Djibouti. Topics could include Lake Assal, the limestone chimneys beside Lake Abbe, and nomad encampments.
4. Explore Djibouti on Google Maps. (Check it in advance.)

help at a glance

Ideas for plenaries

Plan plenaries for strategic points throughout the lesson, as well as at the end.

Mid-lesson

1   Look back at the map on page 118 of the students' book. Ask: Is Djibouti's location better than Somalia's, or Eritrea's? Why? / Why not? (One big advantage of Djibouti over the others is its stability.)

2   Population: Djibouti, about 906 000; Birmingham, about 1 074 000. Ask: Is it strange having a country with a smaller population than a city? Any comments?

3   Ask: How much can you say about the climate of Djibouti? Look back at page 122 of the students' book.

4   About 70% of the population of Djibouti lives in the capital city. Why is that figure so high? Why don't more people live out in the countryside? See if you can give reasons.

End-of-lesson

5   Djibouti is in a great location. Ask: Has that made everyone rich?

6   *A good education can help people to escape from poverty.* Discuss!

7   Ask: What advantages does Djibouti have? What disadvantages? Make two lists.

8   Ask: Can you think of other countries, or cities, that are in great locations? Name them, and say what's good about their locations.

Further class and homework opportunities

Suggestion 42 on page 165 of this book

geog.1 workbook, page 69

geog.1 Kerboodle: see lesson presentation, worksheets, and end-of-lesson assessment

Answers to 'Your turn'

1   Djibouti is the *smallest* country in the Horn of Africa. It is in a brilliant *location*. It sits where the *Gulf of Aden* meets the *Red Sea*. So it can earn a lot of *money* from *ships*.

2   Expect students to label the Red Sea and Gulf of Aden.

3   High unemployment (over 50%); about 75% of people living in poverty, and 40% very poor (living on less than $2 a day); most food needs to be imported, and is therefore expensive.

4   They will be better able to take up skilled jobs, including with foreign companies setting up in Djibouti. They will be more able to start their own companies. They might become teachers, doctors, nurses, engineers, IT experts, and so on – all of whom will help Djibouti.

5   Taxi drivers; staff (managers, cooks, cleaning staff, maintenance staff, receptionists) in hotels, restaurants, and cafes; guides; staff in car rental agencies and tourist offices; laundry workers; people making souvenirs; people producing food for tourists.

6   The adverts could stress the importance of its location by the Red Sea, and its port.

It could mention the attractions of the country: for example, Lake Assal, and beaches. It could say the government is offering incentives such as low-cost or free sites, low taxes.

How is the Horn of Africa doing?

help at a glance

About this unit

This unit presents data to explore, for the countries in the Horn of Africa. Data for the UK are given for comparison.

Key points

- You can learn a lot about a country by studying data.
- GDP per person (PPP) gives an idea of how well off countries are.
- GDP stands for Gross Domestic Product. One way to calculate it is to add up how much everyone in a country earns in a year. (There are other ways.) It is always given in dollars.
- GDP per person is the GDP divided by the population.
- A dollar can buy more in one country than another. So GDP per person is then adjusted for purchasing power parity (PPP) to allow countries to be compared fairly.
- Low GDP per person (PPP) is a sign of poverty, and is linked to issues such as lack of safe water, electricity and sanitation, poor nutrition, poor healthcare, poor education, a lower life expectancy, and so on.
- Overall, the countries of the Horn have a low GDP per person (PPP); they are poor. But today they are developing quite quickly.

Key vocabulary

data, gross domestic product, GDP per person (PPP), life expectancy

Skills practised in 'Your turn'

- Numeracy skills: q1–q5, analyse data in a table; q2, calculate
- Literacy skills: q3, define; q6, explain difference in meaning; q9, decipher, and write, a succinct message
- Thinking skills: q7, q8, explain; q9, decide on a suitable message

Unit outcomes

By the end of this unit most students should be able to:

- explain the terms given in 'Key vocabulary' above
- name the countries of the Horn in order of population, and say which has a larger population than the UK
- say that the population of the Horn is mainly rural – with Djibouti an exception; a high percentage of Djibouti's population is urban, like the UK
- say that a low GDP per person is a sign of poverty: and it is linked to poor healthcare, a lack of access to safe water, lowered life expectancy, and so on.
- say that the countries of the Horn are poor overall; their GDP per person (PPP) is much lower than for the UK
- say that people in the Horn have a lower life expectancy than people in the UK

Ideas for a starter

1 With books closed, ask: Overall, do you think that the Horn of Africa is a wealthy region, or a poor one? What gave you that impression?

2 With books closed, say: Imagine you are flying round the world on a magic carpet, dropping into each country for a quick visit. What kinds of things might tell you whether a country is well off, or not? List answers on the board to return to later. Can they be grouped?

3 Ask: Where was your school uniform made? Look at the label. Would it be good for the Horn of Africa if it were made there? Why? How would it get to you?

Ideas for plenaries

Plan plenaries for strategic points throughout the lesson, as well as at the end.

Mid-lesson

1   Spend some time exploring the data in the table. For example, ask, which country of the Horn has the lowest urban population? Which has the highest GDP per capita? Why do you think that is? (The port and military bases.)

2   Ask: Who can explain what GDP means? GDP per person? GDP per person (PPP)? Are the values likely to rise or fall, for the countries of the Horn?

3   If you did starter 2: Look at the list of points at the bottom of page 136, about what you are likely to find in poorer countries. Ask: Do any match what we wrote on the board?

4   Look at the photos at the top of page 97 of the students' book. Ask: Who set up the oil rig? Who set up the shoe factory? Why did local people not set them up?

5   Ask: Why would a Chinese company come all the way from China to set up a shoe factory in Ethiopia? Who can think of reasons? (Low wages; big population in Ethiopia so big local market for shoes; can export to other African countries, and further afield; plenty of people looking for work; plenty of leather from livestock. Overall, profitable!)

End-of-lesson

6   Lots of foreign companies are setting up factories in the Horn of Africa, and exploring for oil and gas. Ask: Is that a good thing? Is there anything else you'd like to know, before you decide?

7   Ask: Overall, do you think the Horn of Africa will be better off, 15 years from now?

8   Ask students to think of all the things they have learned about Africa, over Chapters 6 and 7.
    –   Which was the most surprising?
    –   Which was the most interesting?
    –   How has your view of Africa changed?
    –   How has your view of geography changed?

Further class and homework opportunities

Suggestions 43–48 on page 165 of this book

geog.1 workbook, page 70

geog.1 Kerboodle: see lesson presentation, worksheets, and end-of-lesson assessment

Answers to 'Your turn'

1   Expect students to include the biggest difference of all: GDP per person (PPP).

2   a   i $600   ii $2700   iii $37 500
    b   62.5 times bigger!

3   In all of them.

4   Djibouti

5   Djibouti, Somalia

6   Unemployed: no paid work. Underemployed: not enough work, or not making full use of the person's skills.

7   Often it's people of working age who go off to fight – and they may be breadwinners. They may get killed, leaving families in great poverty. Homes, hospitals, government buildings, roads, and other infrastructure may get destroyed. Schools and universities may close down so young people miss out on education. People may be driven from their land so can't plant or harvest crops. Young children may lose parents. Companies may close down so people lose their jobs. Afterwards, people may be unable to work together in harmony.

8   a   The country can use the oil and gas to produce electricity, and create a stable electricity supply. Petrol is obtained from oil. The country will save money on importing oil and gas, which are expensive. Instead it may be able to export them.

    b   They provide jobs. People can use their pay to buy better food, and send their children to school. The factory may make things that local people need (which then don't have to be imported), or things to export. The government will earn money from taxes.

    c   They make it easier for people and companies to move goods to places where they can sell them. Also people can reach workplaces, schools, hospitals, and relatives more easily. It becomes easier to develop tourism.

    d   Fewer babies die. Fewer mothers die in childbirth. Sick people are more likely to recover. Families do not have to rely only on themselves to treat illness. Life expectancy will rise.

Most of these suggestions are addressed to your students. Where research or further resources are needed, the internet will almost certainly provide the answer.

The suggestions are graded *, **, *** according to level of difficulty. Some are suitable for all levels, and can be differentiated by outcome.

Meet the Horn of Africa

1 **Colour in** On a blank political map of Africa, colour in and label the four countries of the Horn. Mark and label their capital cities. Then mark in the Equator, Tropic of Cancer, and Tropic of Capricorn. Label the ocean / gulf / sea off the Horn. Add the flag of each country, and name their official languages. *

2 **Choose a country and** … create a photomontage for it. Include people, places – cities and countryside, physical features, food, clothing, homes, cultural buildings, and objects. List what is shown in the pictures. */**/***

3 **Google Maps** Explore the Horn of Africa on Google Maps, in a plenary session. What is the overall impression? See if you can zoom in on the capital cities. */**/***

4 **How big?** Write these on board as a list: UK, 244 000 sq km; Ethiopia, 1 127 130 sq km; Somalia, 637 660 sq km; Eritrea, 117 600 sq km; Djibouti, 23 000 sq km. Compared to the UK: How many times larger is Ethiopia? How many times larger is Somalia? How much smaller is Djibouti? **/***

5 **Selam and Lucy** Two famous fossils of early species, related to humans, found in Ethiopia. (Selam was found in the area shown in the photo on page 119 of the students' book.) Find out more about Selam and Lucy. ***

The Horn of Africa: physical features

6 **Physical features from space** … Find the Ethiopian Highlands on Google Maps. What does the green on the image tell you? Look at the Afar Triangle. Does it show up clearly? Find Lake Tana, and see if you can track the Blue Nile from the south end of the lake until it joins the White Nile. (It loops a lot.) Then follow the Nile all the way to the Mediterranean. */**/***

7 **Erta Ale volcano**… Find it on Google Maps. It has several craters. What is all the black stuff? Find photos of it too. When did it last erupt? */**/***

8 **Dallol volcano** … Find it on Google Maps, and find other pictures too. It does not look much like a volcano. The volcanic activity is due to magma intrusion into beds of mineral salts below ground. Water full of dissolved salts is driven to the surface. It evaporates, leaving colourful salt structures. */**/***

9 **About the Ogaden** What is the Ogaden like? How many people live there? What grows there? It suffers famine from time to time. Why? It also suffers conflict. Why? Can you get photos? ***

10 **Rift Valley** What is a *rift*? Why do you think the Rift Valley is called that?

11 **Plan a geography expedition** to the Horn of Africa. Create an itinerary and route map. Prepare a kit list. Then design a poster, to get other students to sign up for the trip. */**/***

12 **Horn word search** Create a word search for the countries of the Horn, their capitals, and physical features. Try it out on a partner. For an extra challenge, you could write the letters in reverse order. */**

13 **Ethiopia's national parks** Ethiopia has a number of national parks. The oldest is the Awash National Park. Visit it (via the internet). What do you see? Show us your photos. **/***

The Horn of Africa: climate

14 **Climate graphs** Look in Google Images for each of the four capital cities. Choose graphs with only one temperature line (average daily temperature) for simplicity. Ask students to compare them. Which is the hottest city in summer (e.g. July)? Which is coolest? Why? Which is hottest / coolest in December? In which city does the average temperature change least? Which gets most rain? Which gets least? Do they all have a rainy season? Do any have two rainy seasons? There's plenty of geography here! */**/***

15 **Famine** Failing rains may lead to famine. When was the last famine in the Horn of Africa? Write a report. **/***

16 **Biomes** Turn back to the map on page 114 of the students' book. Which biomes does the Horn of Africa have? Note the rainforest biome, in the Ethiopian Highlands. But over 90% of Ethiopia's rainforest has now been cut down. **/***

17 **The loss of Ethiopia's rainforest** Almost all gone – and famine in the Horn of Africa has contributed. Find out more. Present your findings as an article for a geography website. ***

18 **Population density** On the internet you'll find more detailed maps of population density, with many more shades, for Africa. Display one. Look at the pattern of population density in the Horn. **/***

Coffee farming in Ethiopia

19 Write a story board for a 30-second video to encourage people to buy Ethiopian coffee. */**/***

20 Write a poem or song/ rap to encourage people to use Fair Trade products. */**/***

21 **Interview Abel** What will you ask him about life as a coffee farmer? What will he answer? You could work in pairs. */**/***

22 **Black gold** This video about coffee-growing in Ethiopia, the world coffee market, and the plight of coffee farmers, can be bought and downloaded online. It offers many insights into the coffee farmers' lives. (You may want to show only some sections – but it may be useful for other years too.) */**/***

23 Coffee in the shops Design, and then use, a form for collecting data about coffee on sale in a supermarket (visit in person, or online). Where does it come from? Any from Ethiopia? Any Fair Trade? Decide how to show the data. Include a map! You could work in groups. */**/***

24 Coffee map Create a map showing the top ten coffee-growing countries around the world. Mark in the Equator and tropics. Are all ten countries within the tropics? What does this say about the needs of the coffee tree? **/***

25 Ups and downs Download a chequered board, and help students design a coffee-farming game, based on 'good' and 'bad' events. For example … A Fair Trade company offers to buy your beans. Drought ruins your crop. Your child falls ill, and treatment costs a lot. The big coffee companies cut the price they pay for beans. There is a bumper crop in Vietnam. Floods block the road to market. A new road is built to the coffee co-operative. ***

26 Fair trade Find out more about the Fair Trade movement, the pay producers receive, and the kinds of Fair Trade goods on sale. Tell the class. */**/***

Life as a nomad

27 For Safiyo Safiyo and her family will continue to be nomads, moving with their animals. What could be done to make their lives better? For example, would portable solar power panels help? See how many ideas you can come up with. **/***

28 A week as a nomad Write a diary for a week you spend with nomads in Somalia. Think of the quiet, the night sky full of stars, the noise of the animals, the food.

29 Nomad essentials The nomads do not carry much. List a set of essentials for them, in order of importance, most important first. */**/***

Working as a salt miner

30 Images from the Danakil Depression If not used already as a starter, show images of the Danakil Depression, and salt mining. */**/***

31 Ten years later You are Dejen. It is ten years later. What is your life like now? Write the class a letter. */**/***

32 Compare and contrast! Display images of mining for rock salt in the UK, and in Ethiopia. Annotate the images, saying what the similarities and differences are. **/***

33 Pulling Africa apart Tell the class more about why Africa is being pulled apart down the Afar Triangle and Rift Valley. Three plates, which meet at Lake Abbe in Djibouti, are pulling apart. */**/***

Life on the coast

34 Pirates on trial Two or three students take the role of captured pirates. Two groups become lawyers for the prosecution and the defence. The rest of the class acts as the jury. Will the pirates be punished, or set free? */**/***

35 Captain Phillips Show extracts from this film, based on a true story about a ship's captain, and Somalian pirates. */**/***

36 No more piracy You are the new Minister for the Coast, in the government of Somalia. Other countries are putting pressure on you to put an end to piracy. What will you do? Write a plan. */**/***

37 Fishing in your EEZ There are lots of fish in your EEZ. Will you ban fishing boats from other countries? Or will you ask them to pay a fee? Will you limit how much they can fish? How will you keep an eye on them? */**/***

38 Are EEZs fair? Is it fair that coastal countries have an EEZ, reaching out for 370 km? Hold a class debate. */**/***

In the city: Addis Ababa

39 My time in Addis You are visiting Addis Ababa. Write a blog to describe your first few days. (You may need to do some research.) */**/***

40 Design homes for Addis Design a cheap and simple house to be built for newcomers to the city. Start by listing what you think the basic requirements should be. Remember – cheap! */**/***

41 Some Ethiopian history Up until 1974, Ethiopia had an emperor, and an elite group of wealthy people owned all the land. Now the government owns all the land, and leases it out. What happened? ***

Djibouti: a great location

42 Plan a trip to Djibouti When will you go? (Perhaps you should look at a climate graph.) What will you see? Where will you stay? Where will you fly from? **/***

How is the Horn of Africa doing?

43 Who's famous? Choose a famous person from the Horn of Africa – living or dead – and write a short biography. Perhaps an athlete, or a model, or an Emperor! */**/***

44 Invest! Write a 30-second appeal to companies from other countries to open factories and branches in the Horn of Africa. Use Movie Maker? */**/***

45 Conflict! One thing that has held back the Horn of Africa is conflict – both within and between the four countries. Print out a map of the Horn countries. See if you can add notes about conflict in the last 50 years or so. ***

46 Mastermind Teams create a quiz about the region. Other teams answer. Award prizes? */**/***

47 Mind map Produce a mind map for the Horn of Africa, using coloured markers on sugar paper. */**/***

48 Alphabet run Do an illustrated alphabet run for the Horn of Africa, with something for each letter. */**/***

Glossary

A

abrasion – scraping away material

abstract – pump out water to be used as a water supply (from a river or aquifer)

aerial photo – a photo taken from the air

aquifer – underground rock that holds a large amount of fresh water

arête – a sharp ridge, shaped by a glacier

asteroid – large chunks of rock that orbit the Sun; it is thought that they are material left over when planets formed

asylum seeker – a person who flees to another country for safety, and asks for permission to stay there

atmosphere – the layer of gas around Earth

B

bedload – stones and other fragments that roll or bounce along a river bed

Big Bang – the explosion of energy that led to the formation of the Universe

biome – a very large area with a similar climate, plants, and animals

C

capital city – the city where the country's government is based

climate – what the weather in a place is usually like, over the year

condense – to change from gas to liquid

confluence – where two rivers join

continent – one of Earth's great land masses; there are seven continents

contour line – line on a map joining places that are the same height above sea level

country – humans have divided continents into political units called countries

core – the inner layer of Earth, made mainly of iron plus a little nickel

corrie – a hollow where a glacier started; corries are also called cirques, and cwms

crags – steep rugged cliffs

crust – the thin outer layer of Earth, made of rock

D

deposit – to drop material; rivers deposit sediment as they approach the sea

depression – an area of sunken land

desertification – where land is being turned into desert, often through overuse

DNA – deoxyribonucleic acid; it forms the genes that tell our cells how to develop

drought – there is less rain than usual, so there is not enough water for our needs

drumlin – a long smooth hill shaped like the back of a spoon, created by a glacier

E

earthquake – the shaking of Earth's crust, caused by sudden rock movement

economic – about money and business

economy – all the business activity going on in a country; if more goods and services are being produced and sold, we say the economy is growing

economic migrants – people who move to a new place to find work, and to improve their standard of living

EEZ – exclusive economic zone; the area off a country's coast, where only that country has the right to fish, explore for oil, and so on

embankment – a bank of earth or concrete built up on a river bank, to stop the river flooding

emigrant – a person who leaves his or her own country to settle in another country

eon – the biggest block of time in the geological timescale

Equator – an imaginary line around the middle of Earth (at 0° latitude)

erosion – the wearing away of rock, stones and soil by rivers, waves, wind or glaciers

erratic – a large rock that's different from the types of rock around it; it was carried there by a glacier

evaporation – the change from liquid to gas

evolution – the process by which new species of living things develop

exploit – to make use of a place, or people, or things, for your own benefit

F

famine – when food is scarce; people may starve to death

flash flood – a sudden flood usually caused by a very heavy burst of rain

flood – an overflow of water from the river

flood defences – structures built to prevent flooding; for example an embankment

floodplain – flat land around a river that gets flooded when the river overflows

fossil fuel – coal, oil, natural gas

freeze-thaw weathering – where water freezes in cracks in rock, making them bigger; eventually the rock breaks up

fresh water – the water found in rivers, lakes, wells, and streams; it is not salty

G

galaxy – a group of billions of stars

geological timescale – it shows the time since Earth began

geologist – a scientist who studies rocks, earthquakes, and so on

glacier – a river of ice

glacial – to do with glaciers

glaciated – covered by glaciers, now or in the past

global warming – the rise in average temperatures around the world

gorge – a narrow valley with steep sides

gravity – the force of attraction that holds planets in the solar system, and holds us on Earth

grazing – land with grass and other vegetation, where animals can feed

grid reference – a set of numbers, or numbers and letters, that tells you where to find something on a map

ground moraine – the material a glacier drops all over the ground when it melts

groundwater – rainwater that has soaked down through the ground and filled up the cracks in the rock below

gulf – a large area of ocean that is partly enclosed by land

H

hanging valley – a valley that hangs above a larger one; if it has a river, the water will pour down to the larger valley as a waterfall

Homo sapiens – our species; there were other species of humans before us

hydroelectricity – electricity generated when flowing water drives a turbine

I

ice age – a time when Earth's average temperature was lower than usual, and glaciers spread

ice shelf – a sheet of ice that is attached to land, but floats on the ocean

immigrant – a person who moves here from another country, to live

impermeable – does not let water pass through

independence – when a country governs itself; the European colonies in Africa fought for independence

Industrial Revolution – the period (about 1760 – 1840) when many new machines were invented, and many factories built

infiltration – soaking into the ground

international – to do with more than one country

invader – enters a country to attack it

irrigate – to water crops

L

land bridge – land that is exposed when sea levels fall; people can walk across it

landform – a feature formed by erosion or deposition (for example a gorge)

lateral moraine – the material a glacier deposits along the sides of its route

latitude – how far a place is north or south of the Equator; it is measured in degrees

lava – melted rock from a volcano

leeward – sheltered from the wind

life expectancy – how many years a new baby can expect to live for, on average

local – to do with the area around you

longitude – how far a place is east or west of the Prime Meridian; it is measured in degrees

long profile – the side view of a river from source to mouth, showing how the slope changes

M

magma – melted rock below Earth's surface; at the surface it is called lava

mantle – the middle layer of Earth, between the crust and the core

manufacturing – making things in factories

mass extinction – when a large number of species die off; for example because an ice age arrives

meander – a bend in a river

media – forms of communication, such as TV, radio, newspapers, the internet

meltwater – water from a melting volcano

mental map – a map you carry in your head

meteorite – a chunk of rock that lands on Earth, from space

migrant – a person who moves to another part of the country, or another country, often just to work for a while

moraine – material deposited by a glacier

multicultural – has different ethnic groups

N

national – to do with the whole country (for example the national anthem)

nomad – a person who rears animals, and travels with them to find grazing

North Atlantic Drift – a warm current in the Atlantic Ocean; it keeps the weather on the west coast of Britain mild in winter

O

oxbow lake – a lake formed when a loop in a river gets cut off

OS maps – detailed maps of places drawn by the Ordnance Survey, to scale

P

permeable – lets water soak through

persecute – to punish or treat cruelly (for example because of race or religion)

plan – a map of a small area (such as the school, or a room) drawn to scale

plateau – an area of fairly flat high land

plunge pool – deep pool below a waterfall

population – the number of people living in a place

population density – the average number of people living in a place, per square kilometre

precipitation – water falling from the sky (as rain, sleet, hail, snow)

prevailing winds – the ones that blow most often; in the UK they are south west winds (they blow from the south west)

Prime Meridian – an imaginary line that circles Earth from pole to pole; it is at 0° longitude

pyramidal peak – a sharp peak on a mountain, created by glacial erosion

R

rainforest – has lush vegetation, with many different species of plants and animals

refugee – a person who has been forced to flee from danger (for example from war)

ribbon lake – long thin lake in a trough created by glacial erosion

river basin – the land from which water drains into the river

rural area – countryside, where people live on farms and in small villages

Glossary

S

savanna – has grassy plains with scattered trees

scale – the ratio of the distance on a map to the real distance

sediment – a layer of material (stones, sand and mud) deposited by a river

semi-desert – dry, and not much vegetation

settlement – a place where people live; it could be a hamlet, village, town or city

sewage works – where the waste liquid from our homes is cleaned up, before it is put back in the river

sketch map – a simple map to show what a place is like, or how to get there; it is not drawn to scale

slum – area of very poor housing

solar system – made up of our Sun, the planets, their moons, and asteroids and other floating objects

source – the starting point of a river

sparsely populated – not many live there

species – a type of plant or animal

spot height – the exact height, in metres, at a spot on an OS map (look for a number)

stereotyped – about fixed opinions people have, that do not reflect reality

striations – grooves in rock, caused by abrasion when glaciers flowed over it

suspension – small particles of rock and soil carried along in a river

T

tarn – lakes in corries are often called tarns in the Lake District

terminal moraine – the ridge of material dropped at the front of a melting glacier

till – a mixture of rocks, clay, sand and other sediment dropped by a glacier

transport – to carry things along

tributary – a river that flows into a larger one

tundra – a cold region where the ground is deeply frozen; only the surface thaws in summer, allowing small plants to grow

U

underemployed – has paid work, but not enough, or not making full use of skills

unemployed – has no paid work

urban area – a built-up area (town or city

U-shaped valley – a valley shaped like the letter U, carved out by a glacier

V

valley – low land, with higher land on each side; it was carved out by a river or glacier

volcano – a place where melted rock erupts

V-shaped valley – a valley shaped like the letter V, carved out by a river

W

water cycle – water evaporates from the sea, falls as rain, and returns to the sea in rivers

waterfall – where a river or stream flows over a steep drop

water table – the upper surface of groundwater

water vapour – water in gas form

watershed – an imaginary line separating one river basin from the next

weather – the state of the atmosphere – for example how warm or wet it is

weathering – the breaking down of rock, caused mainly by the weather; it turns into soil in the end

windward – facing into the wind